INTRODUCTION TO BIOENERGETICS: THERMODYNAMICS FOR THE BIOLOGIST

A LEARNING PROGRAM FOR STUDENTS OF THE BIOLOGICAL AND MEDICAL SCIENCES

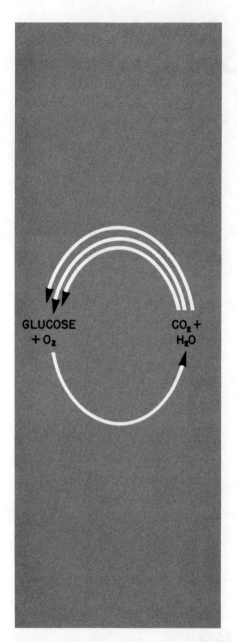

HALVOR N. CHRISTENSEN, Ph.D.

Department of Biological Chemistry
The University of Michigan

RICHARD A. CELLARIUS, Ph.D.

Department of Botany
The University of Michigan

1972

W. B. SAUNDERS COMPANY · PHILADELPHIA · LONDON · TORONTO

W. B. Saunders Company: West Washington Square
Philadelphia, Pa. 19105

12 Dyott Street
London, WC1A 1DB

833 Oxford Street
Toronto 18, Ontario

165635

Introduction to Bioenergetics: Thermodynamics for the Biologist ISBN 0-7216-2588-6

Print No.: 9 8 7 6 5 4 3 2 1

B/10167

Preface

We have been led to conclude that earlier programs in this series have served as models to convince the student of biology that he can master physicochemical areas of his subject rather well even if his curriculum has unfortunately not permitted him a full sequence of courses in chemistry. The subjects of the acid-base dissociation of complex biological molecules and the kinetics of catalytic processes provided these models. Although we think the present program will confirm the confidence accrued by its predecessors, it is obviously a more ambitious program. Accordingly, we see it not as another, parallel model, but instead as an exploitation, so to speak, under the student's direction, of the confidence which we presume he has otherwise gained, whereby he can also teach himself what may be regarded as the central discipline offered to the biologist by theoretical chemistry and physics.

Programing of the subject of thermodynamics with this objective in mind has cost us not less than twice the effort and reflection called forth by each of the other subjects. We suspect that the program will require in a similar proportion an extra effort on the part of the biology student who has economized a good deal in his study of chemistry. We don't mean merely that 14 hours instead of seven may be required for each full perusal, but also that extra effort and motivation will be required to repeat the study of sections that prove difficult and to supplement use of the program by other methods of study. Our experience suggests that a small proportion of biology students might even need to direct themselves to a strong first-year chemistry text for review of background concepts. If the student can only succeed in maintaining a sufficient confidence and motivation ("energy of activation") through the first 70-odd items, covering the First and Second Laws of Thermodynamics, we believe he will find spontaneous motivation to learning beyond that point; that is, we believe the overall free-energy change will prove favorable. By providing support to the student's motivation, comprehension and ancillary study, the instructor (if any) who is guiding the use of the program can minimize what we may call kinetic failures in the early stages of the study. Undoubtedly other students with training in physical chemistry, who are using the program for remedial review, can expect to function as "isolated systems," without informational or motivational support from external sources, including examinations.

Two aspects of our approach to basic thermodynamic concepts deserve special mention. The first is the decision to accept the recent recommendation of the International Union of Pure and Applied Chemistry* to define W as the work done *on* the system rather than the work done *by* the system. This changes the mathematical statement of the First Law of Thermodynamics to read $\Delta U = Q + W$ instead of the more common $\Delta U = Q - W$. Although the change may cause some difficulty for those who are more familiar with the traditional convention, we feel that it has a major advantage. All other thermodynamic quantities are defined so that a positive value implies an increase of that quantity in the system under consideration. We feel to use the same convention for the work done is pedagogically better, and that, in the long run, doing so will assist the comprehension of a conceptually difficult subject.

The second feature that deserves mention is the approach to the Second Law of Thermodynamics, the entropy, and the free energy. We have chosen first to focus attention on the work required for a given change occurring at constant temperature and to defer introduction of the entropy. (In fact, although we do not recommend his doing so, the learner is given the option of omitting altogether the development of

*Pure and Applied Chemistry, 21;1 (1970).

the subject of the entropy.) The reader is thus led directly from the Second Law to the most important feature of chemical thermodynamics, the free energy, which we first define in terms of the minimal amount of work required to drive a reaction at constant temperature. We should acknowledge our debt to Spanner,* who points out the possibility of this approach, even though his text actually introduces the entropy first. We hope by this decision, without resorting either to complex analyses of the properties of Carnot cycles or to "pulling things out of thin air," to have succeeded in showing the student that the most fundamental and powerful thermodynamic tools may be derived from the simple statement of experience embodied in the Second Law.

From time to time the authors have discussed with their editors the notion of economically binding a duplicate of the programed text within the same cover, to persuade the student both to write out the answers in the spaces provided and to repeat the operation for all sections not fully mastered during the first passage. Unfortunately, too many enterprising pairs of students undoubtedly would bisect such double programs with a razor blade, thus largely eliminating the stimulus of that plan; hence we have had to leave to the student the problem of how to implement our sincere recommendation that for optimal learning he actually solve each problem and write out each response.

The most logical sequence of use of the four modular programs of this series is probably: *pH and Dissociation, Thermodynamics, Enzyme Kinetics* and *Neutrality Control in the Living Organism*. Pedagogically, this order also has the advantage that mastering the first program may build the learner's confidence for the more ambitious second. The programs have been prepared, however, to permit independent use of any one, two or three of them, cross-references between them being sparse and optional.

Let us then say something to the persons who will make decisions, either for themselves or for other learners, about how much of this program to assign and what parts to omit:

*D.C. Spanner, *Introduction to Thermodynamics* (Academic Press, New York, 1964).

The program may advantageously be studied as if it were three successive programs, as follows: *Introduction* through *Second Law*, Items 1 to 81; *Chemical Reactions* through *Oxidation-Reduction Potentials*, Items 82 to 179; *Membrane Equilibria* and *The Steady State*, Items 180 to 263. Other suitable points for interruptions will be obvious from the major headings.

The total of all the items included here corresponds to our provisional notion of a balanced treatment of the subject for the biologist. Although the extent of abbreviation that can successfully be obtained has obvious limits, we have tried to indicate ways in which the study could be shortened without serious discontinuity by as much as 16 per cent or (by one deplorable omission) even by as much as another 30 per cent. We have tried, in identifying such possible omissions, not to impoverish the remainder of the program by eliminating illustrative applications, but instead to imagine circumscriptions either in the needs or in the preparation of some of the learners who might use the program. For example, we have supposed that some students may not be prepared to use a differential equation to define the chemical potential; we have imagined that students might in some cases dispense with the study of the method of determining ΔG for a reaction from the difference in the free energies of formation of the reactants and the products (Items 117–121); or with the study of concentration cells (Items 174–179); or with the derivation and application of the van't Hoff equation for the osmotic pressure (Items 203–211). Students might even accept the concept of the change in entropy without studying its basis (Items 53–72), or conceivably membrane phenomena and active transport (Items 175–263) might fall outside their biological interests. They might not be prepared by prior or simultaneous study of biochemistry to compare the structures and functions of high-energy phosphorus compounds (Items 127–131).

Having constructed the program to identify some such subjects that can be omitted without absolute loss of continuity, the authors nevertheless recommend only minimal omissions, and transfer to those who decide to make a given omission the responsibility for that decision. We also warn the learner not to regard items marked here for possible omission as less important than starred items. For your goals, these may be especially important items. We can illustrate this view with comments about two sections suggested for possible omission:

1. No doubt some teachers will assert very reasonably that it would be absurd to omit the section on "high-energy bonds" and that it should instead be emphasized much more than it is, perhaps along with the subject of energetic uncoupling (see *Appendix A,* page 211). Unfortunately, we cannot anticipate how much access the student will have to information about the substances involved and their metabolic roles, a subject that obviously cannot be presented *in extenso* here. Hence, only the learner and his teacher (if any) will know whether the opportunity of the program to reinforce thermodynamic conceptions for that area is large or small.

2. A perusal of the program will persuade the reader that the authors don't really want anyone to omit the section on membrane phenomena. Instead we feel that thermodynamics offers the biologist some of its largest rewards in that area.

With the above comments we hope that our suggestions for possible omissions will not prejudice the student against certain sections of the program.

So many colleagues and students at this university and elsewhere have now helped us by critical reading or experimental use of this program and its precursors that it would represent a gratuitous and bulky exploitation of many names and inevitably the omission of others to attempt a list of all those to whom we are indebted for assistance. Finally, let us add that the perfecting of a learning program never ends and that we are most receptive to criticisms and suggestions.

Ann Arbor, Michigan   Halvor N. Christensen
            Richard A. Cellarius

Comments to the Learner on Using This Program.

You will soon note that some of the exercises of this program require a great deal more calculation and time than others. You should not expect to proceed quickly and evenly, nor to learn the subject successfully if you omit the calculations, or if you merely imagine yourself filling in part or all of the responses.

You can turn quickly to the logarithm table on the inside of the back cover and to the facing table of constants, conversion factors and equations, for use in solving problems. Furthermore, you must take your satisfactions in the quality of your response (imperfect or otherwise) with due regard to the difficulty of the item. In any event, if you want to learn as you proceed, be sure you require yourself to write out formally the choices and solutions for each item, preventing yourself from accidentally seeing the answer printed in the book by covering it with the "slider" attached to the back cover.

The printed responses are of course intended to provide confirmation to the student that he is proceeding alertly and correctly. In some cases the student's answer may be a reasonable alternative to the printed answer. In such cases, the student must give himself credit for being right—clearly it is impossible for us to anticipate every synonym or alternative to the response. Because the learning process is assisted by the satisfactions obtained at each step, a tolerant attitude toward each item and its answer will contribute to your achievement. You must not let yourself be annoyed if some of the frames are absurdly easy, or if the information requested would be unreasonable were it not for cues internal to the item, or received from your background information, or even by an untraceable intuition. When all factors fail you, don't stop to ask angrily, "How was I supposed to know that!"—just forge ahead. (Nothing is as deadly to programing as a built-in defense to that question—for example, through a tedious set of unnecessary back-references within the items!) Avoid the role of critic, because you will assume it to the disadvantage of learning.

The items are of course not examination questions. Although the student can judge by his progress how alertly he is proceeding, he cannot predict well what his subsequent recall will be. On completion of the program, turn to the summary and examination material at the back, and by its use discover which portions of the program will require further study. Some selected test questions are even identified for possible preliminary use after study of the First and Second Laws. Other methods, particularly practice in answering questions out of context and in applying the ideas to new situations, are necessary to a good result. The so-called provocative questions should illustrate with a few scattered examples the rich possibilities for applying thermodynamics to biological phenomena encountered in other studies. Particularly fortunate is the student who is concurrently studying a course in physical and chemical biology in which he can find additional opportunities to apply the ideas of thermodynamics.

A word may be said about the increasing need of the biologist to understand the principal concepts of thermodynamics. This intensified need lies particularly in the understanding of the coupling between biological processes. When can that coupling serve to supply energy? When can the energy supplied suffice? Can the energy flow in either direction? The biologist needs also to understand that the potential energy inherent in a concentration gradient is fundamentally similar to that inherent in chemical structures of a given energy content; also that the flow of a component from one compartment to another can be coupled to the progress of a chemical reaction, and that here also the energy transfer may occur in either direction. The problems that face us now in biology are mainly those of the heterogeneous rather than the homogeneous system, and those who will contribute the most to their solution will combine an interest in physical flows and in the flows of chemical reactions. The rising concern that we conserve energy for our most basic and deeply felt needs requires that we know when we are conserving our potential for getting work done or effecting changes rather than in fact accelerating the increase of entropy. The biologist must of course understand energetics if his biological advice is to be valid.

Contents

CONTENTS

INTRODUCTION TO BIOENERGETICS: THERMODYNAMICS FOR THE BIOLOGIST

*A LEARNING PROGRAM
FOR STUDENTS OF
THE BIOLOGICAL AND
MEDICAL SCIENCES*

INTRODUCTION

1

✻ This program and a partner to it will describe biochemical reactions in two ways:

    A. The present program covers the energy transformations taking place.

    B. The second program* discusses the factors affecting the velocity of the reaction.

The first of these is sometimes called *energetics* and is based on the science of thermodynamics. The second is called *kinetics*. Note that these are entirely different approaches: The first says nothing about the rate at which a process will proceed; it only permits us to determine whether the process is energetically possible, and how much useful energy it may provide to run another process. The second concerns itself only with the rate of a process and not with the state toward which it is tending. Only in late stages of the second program will we combine information from these approaches.

---

*H. N. Christensen and G. Palmer, *Enzyme Kinetics* (W. B. Saunders Co., Philadelphia, 1967). A learning program that may be used to advantage after the present program.

2

✳ Fill in the blanks to show which of these approaches should serve better to answer each of the following questions:

    1. Why is most of the energy of the glucose molecule obtained in the Krebs cycle and not in glycolysis? *Energetics*.

    2. Does H_2CO_3 break down fast enough to permit metabolic CO_2 to be excreted into the atmosphere? *Kinetics*.

    3. Why is energy best conserved for driving other processes when the cytochromes of the electron-transport chain receive and donate electrons in a given sequence? *Energetic*.

2

1. Energetics (A)

2. Kinetics (B)

3. Energetics (A)

3

✱ Students of biology often find the mathematical development of thermodynamics somewhat abstract and isolated from ordinary experience. On the contrary, it is based on experience; the two fundamental laws of thermodynamics were established by observation and cannot be proved mathematically. The sense of abstractness arises because in the thermodynamic approach we must begin by defining our systems rather arbitrarily, and because we must disregard the question of the rates at which events occur.

For example, according to thermodynamics, H_2 and O_2 will combine *spontaneously* with each other; yet they can be held in admixture indefinitely. Similarly, all the molecular, anatomical and functional organization of the living organism should *spontaneously* disappear because of its high energy content. Decide which of the following meanings thermodynamics gives to the word *spontaneously* in these statements:

☐ 1. Readily and without constraint
☑ 2. Without the necessity of external force

3

☑2. Without the necessity of external force

4

✱ Our subject deals with collections of molecules or particles. Such a collection is referred to as a *system*. Thermodynamics describes the energy transformations that may occur within the system and the energy exchanges that may occur between the system and its surroundings. Would we be justified in calling the system plus its surroundings another system? *yes* .

5

✳ We will deal with three types of systems–*open, closed* and *isolated*. An *open system* can exchange both matter and energy with its surroundings, a *closed system* can exchange only energy, and an *isolated system* can exchange neither matter nor energy with its surroundings. Which of these would a living organism ordinarily represent?

X   ~~Closed~~ .

6

✳ The formalism of thermodynamics is set up primarily for either *closed* or *isolated* systems. That is, we usually specify that the system may not exchange matter with its surroundings; we often allow, however, that it may exchange _matter_ with its environment, thereby functioning as a(n) _isolated_ system.

  In Item 4 we noted that a system plus its surroundings make up another, larger system. Even if the former is an open or closed system, we may consider that the system plus its surroundings constitutes a(n) ☑closed ☐isolated system.

4

Yes (since we will again have a collection of molecules or particles)

5

Open

6

energy

closed

☑isolated

WORK, ENERGY AND HEAT: THE FIRST LAW OF THERMODYNAMICS

Definitions

7

✱ First we will define the terms work and heat, without regard to your possible prior familiarity with them. (If the next several items seem very simple to you, you might try skipping to Item 16.)

It takes work to raise a weight from one height to another, as we know from experience. In fact, work is defined in physics as the product of the force necessary to lift a weight, for example, and the distance the weight is raised:

$$\text{Work} = \text{Force} \times \text{Distance}$$

If we attach the weight we have lifted to another equal weight by a suitable pulley system, the second can be raised to the same height by moving the first one down, with essentially no effort on our part. Thus, because of its position the first weight had the capacity to do work, i.e., to lift the second weight. This *capacity to do work* is given the name *energy*, and in this case we use the term *potential energy* because of the stored or latent nature of the energy. After the second weight has been raised, it has gained a certain amount of potential _energy_, and the first weight has _potentially lost_ an equal amount.

8

✳ Another form of mechanical energy is *kinetic* energy, that energy due to the motion of a body. If one of our weights were to fall free instead of lifting a second weight, it would accelerate and the potential energy due to its original position would be converted into the kinetic energy of motion. The science of mechanics tells us that the difference in its ___*potential*___ energy at the top and bottom is equal to its ___*kinetic*___ energy as it reaches the bottom of its free fall.

9

✳ We note incidentally that the falling weight is capable of doing work, such as driving a nail, and that the work it can do is equal to the ___Wt × dist___ at the bottom of its fall.

ₓ *Kinetic Energy*

10

✳ We cannot be sure, just because we *do work on a system,* that we will end up with a system of increased *potential* or *kinetic* energy, as we did when we lifted the weight in Item 7. To slide a weight across the floor, we must apply force, i.e., we must also do work on the weight. After the weight has been moved, it has no greater capacity to do work than it had before, in spite of the work we have done to move it. Particularly if we had moved the weight rapidly, we might observe that a temperature increase had occurred. We often say, in this case, that the work we did has been converted into ☐temperature ☑heat.

7

energy

lost

8

potential

kinetic

9

kinetic energy

10

heat

11

will also

11

✶ The concept of heat derives directly from that of temperature. If two objects (or systems) at different temperatures are placed in contact, sooner or later they reach a common, intermediate temperature. We can determine how much heat has been lost or gained by measuring how much the temperature of each has changed. From common experience we know that we ☑will also ☑will not need to take into account the mass and composition of a body in deciding how much heat has been transferred to it.

12

✶ We can define the quantity of heat, Q, absorbed by a system as equal to a positive constant (C, the heat capacity) times the temperature increase, ΔT, during the period of heat transfer, thus:

$$Q = C(\Delta T) = C\left(T_{final} - T_{initial}\right)$$

If the temperature decreases, ΔT is negative. Therefore Q will be ☐positive ☑negative and heat will be ☑given off ☐absorbed by the system. From ordinary experience, we know that the value of C will ☑depend on ☐be independent of the mass and composition of the system.

13

✳ The usual unit in which the quantity of heat absorbed is measured is the *calorie*. It is defined as the amount of heat that will increase the temperature of 1 gm of water from 14.5°C to 15.5° C. Accordingly, the value of C for water is, by this definition, ____/____ calorie(s) per gram per degree Centigrade.

14

✳ The observation that moving the weight across the floor produces a temperature increase suggested that the work we did was converted into heat, rather than into mechanical energy. When a given amount of mechanical work is done under conditions such that all the energy is converted into heat, the amount of heat produced can be measured precisely, and it always turns out to be the same. This value is known as the *mechanical equivalent of heat;* 1 calorie is produced for every 4.1840 joules of work done.* Because of the constancy of the mechanical equivalent of heat we speak of heat as a form of energy.

Note carefully: Did we say in this item that if 1 calorie of heat is available, 4.1840 joules of work can be accomplished with it? _____.

*Because of this equivalency and to reduce the number of units in use, the International Union of Pure and Applied Chemistry (*Pure and Applied Chemistry*, *21*:1 [1970]) has recommended that the use of the calorie as a unit "be progressively discouraged and abandoned" in favor of the *joule* (*J*). Because the bulk of thermodynamic data for chemical reactions is tabulated in calories, however, in this program we shall continue to use the calorie as the primary unit of energy.

12

negative

given off

depend on

13

one

14

No (The converse
was stated: 4.1840
joules of work can
lead to production
of 1 calorie of heat.)

15

cannot

15

✳ Our rejection of the converse to the stated
mechanical equivalent of heat brings out a
point to be developed later, that heat differs
from other forms of energy in that it ☐ can
☐ cannot be converted completely into
work.

The First Law

16

✳ The First Law of Thermodynamics* says that energy is conserved. Because thermodynamically we have no way of determining the state of zero energy, we cannot measure or even define, in an absolute sense, the total energy of a system. Therefore we must deal with energy changes. In discussing the First Law, then, we first have to define what we mean by the energy change in quantities we can measure (i.e., heat and work). We then can determine the properties of the energy by experimentation and by generalization and logical deduction from the experimental results. (It should be noted that the restriction on determining the zero level holds true for most other thermodynamic functions except the entropy, for which a zero level can be defined. As a result, in this program we almost always will deal with the *change* in energy, entropy, free energy, etc.)

Let us suppose that we picture a system existing in two states, *A* and *B*. For example, the two states might be a rock at the top and at the bottom of a hill, a gas at two different pressures and volumes or a chemical mixture before and after a reaction. We will *define* the energy difference between the two states (namely ΔU or $U_B - U_A$[†]) as the *heat absorbed by the system (Q)* plus *the work done on the system (W)*. By this statement we imply that the energy of a system can change only by exchange of heat or work with its surroundings.

Complete the mathematical statement of the relationship between the energy and the amount of heat and work put into the system.

$$\Delta U = \text{_____}$$

16

The complete equation:

$$\Delta U = Q + W \,^\dagger$$

17

* It has been found experimentally that one can proceed from state A of our system to state B by any path we choose *without any effect on the value of ΔU*, the difference in energy represented by the two states. Does this statement say that the heat absorbed or the work done on the system will also be independent of the route followed from one state to another? _____.

17

No (The values of Q and W depend on the path followed, but must always summate to yield the same value for ΔU.

18

* The statement that, for a system going from one state to another, ΔU is independent of the path, has been found so universally true that we accept it as an axiom of nature—the *First Law of Thermodynamics*. We can take as a mathematical statement of the First Law the equation already developed,

$$\Delta U = \underline{\hspace{2cm}},$$

with the essential condition that ΔU depends ☐only on the initial and final states of the system ☐not only on the initial and final states but also on how they are achieved.

*We will capitalize the words "First Law" and "Second Law" to try to convey to the reader the importance we attribute to them.
† E is frequently used to represent the energy rather than U.
‡ In many textbooks, the First Law is written as $\Delta U = Q - W$, where W refers to the work done *by* the system. The International Union of Pure and Applied Chemistry [*Pure and Applied Chemistry, 21*:1 (1970)] recently has recommended the use of the convention that W is the work done *on* the system, which we have accepted for use in this program. The reader needs to be aware of the widespread use of the earlier convention.

19

✱ A detailed definition of an *isolated* system says that neither *work* nor *heat* is exchanged with the surroundings. It therefore follows from the First Law that the value of ΔU for an isolated system will be _____.

20

✱ When exchanges of energy only are allowed between a system and its surroundings, that is, when we are dealing with ☐a closed ☐an isolated system, it follows from the definitions of Q and W that

$$+ Q_{system} = - Q_{surroundings}$$

and

$$+ W_{system} = - W_{surroundings}$$

Write a similar equation, based on the First Law, showing how ΔU for a system is related to ΔU for its surroundings.

This conclusion is a very natural one, because a system plus its surroundings may be considered to make up a larger, *isolated* system, for which, as we saw in Item 19,

$$\Delta U = \text{_____}$$

18

$$Q + W$$

only on the initial and final states of the system

19

zero

20

a closed

$$\Delta U_{system} = - \Delta U_{surroundings}$$

zero

21

no

21

✳ These manipulations of the First Law, $\Delta U = Q + W$, bring out its essence, that energy cannot be created or destroyed. The First Law is a formal statement of the *principle of the conservation of energy*. When we say that *the energy change of a system is independent of the path followed* from one state to another, not only are we allowing for the interconvertibility of different forms of energy, but we are also specifying that such interconversions have ☐some ☐no effect on the total amount of energy present.

22

✳ The law of the conservation of energy is fundamental to living organisms. The building up of protoplasm involves the construction of molecular structures whose potential energy content is high relative to the energy content of the small molecules which the organism derives from its environment and from which it builds these larger molecules.

This statement means that to build 1 g of protoplasmic mass, an organism must obtain

☐ 1. nutrients containing only as much carbon, nitrogen and other elements as will be contained in 1 g of protoplasm.

☐ 2. substantially larger quantities of nutrients than will supply such elements, because the energy for biosynthesis of protoplasmic molecules must be provided by breakdown of the excess nutrients.

✳ Even to maintain its own mass, an organism must constantly rebuild molecules which are subject to breakdown; it must transport the nutrient molecules to the synthetic site against concentration gradients; it must eliminate water and waste products, by all these energy-requiring processes. In addition, many organisms expend energy in moving and thus doing work on their environments. Particularly for warm-blooded animals, heat energy is lost because of their temperature difference from the environment.

These statements mean that organisms temporarily cut off from their food supply

☐ 1. will cease to grow, and simply retain protoplasmic mass.

☐ 2. must sacrifice protoplasmic constituents and mass to remain alive.

☑2. substantially larger quantities...

23

24

✓2. must sacrifice
protoplasmic...

✱ In the land animal (and particularly in our own case) the body size normally increases only slowly or not at all after an adult age is reached. Check *one or more* of the following devices which appear thermodynamically acceptable to achieve this phenomenon.

☐ 1. An overall balance must be maintained between the intake and the expenditure of energy.

☐ 2. Metabolism should function so that excesses of nutrient intake tend to be diverted to storage forms, such as fat, which can be consumed for energy later, rather than utilized immediately for growth.

(Note that increases of adipose tissue are not considered growth, but increases in muscle and bone are.)

☐ 3. Pathways need to be found by which nutrient molecules can be broken down to the usual waste products with an unusually small energy release.

✱ The energy of a system is the sum of various types of energy: potential, kinetic, thermal, chemical, electrical, and so on. In general, we cannot calculate or determine the total energy. Instead it is sufficient to study the changes in U occurring during various processes. Furthermore, thermodynamics does not attempt to assign origins to the energy of various types in a system. It is true that kinetic theory and statistical mechanics have been able to relate the thermal energy of a system to the kinetic energy of the molecules in it. Similarly, the chemical energy of a system can be attributed to the potential energy inherent in the chemical bonds of its molecules. But thermodynamics restricts itself to the change in the total of these forms of energy.

Check which statement describes best how thermodynamics proceeds:

☐ 1. The total energy of a system is determined without concern for its origin.

☐ 2. The total energy change of a system during a given process is determined, without regard to the change in each type of energy.

☐ 3. The change in each of the various types of energy in a system is determined and these are summated.

☑1. An overall balance must be maintained...

☑2. Metabolism should function... (The third alternative is a thermodynamic impossibility. Pathways leading to exceptional heat loss should however be useful. For example, thyroxin may cause inefficient transfer of energy from electron transfer to *ATP* generation [uncoupling], leading to increased heat losses.)

25

☑2. The total energy
change ... with-
out regard to the
change in each
type...

26

✳ Remembering that the energy of a system
depends on its state ☐irrespective of
☐as well as on the pathway by which
the state was achieved, suppose that a given
reaction transforms a system from one state to
another. Would it be correct to determine ΔU
for this reaction carried out in the most simple
way, and to assume that the same value of
ΔU applies to this change of state no matter
how it is carried out? _____ .

26

irrespective of

Yes (This important
point holds for all
properties that de-
pend only on the
state of a system.
We will make fre-
quent use of it sub-
sequently in this
program.)

Enthalpy

27

✻ An important thermodynamic function related to the energy is the enthalpy, which we will now proceed to introduce in the next five items.

Many processes (both chemical reactions and other processes occurring in living organisms) take place at constant pressure. The properties of these are often such that a change of volume occurs simultaneously. This means that an amount of work equal to $-P\Delta V$ must always be done on the system during the process. (The minus sign is necessary because the volume of the system decreases when such work is done *on* the system.) For these cases, it is convenient to single out and designate as W' all the work done on the system other than that required for the volume change. This term, W' defines the *net* or *useful* work done on the system. If W' is less than zero (negative) then useful work is instead being done by the system on its surroundings.

$$W_P = W'_P - P\Delta V$$

(The subscript is used to indicate that the process occurs at constant pressure.) Recalling that $\Delta U = Q + W$, we can write

$$Q_P + W'_P = Q_P + W_P + P\Delta V$$

$$= \Delta U + \underline{\hspace{2cm}}$$

where all terms on the right of the second equality sign ☐are ☐are not properties of the state of the system.

27

The full equation we
reached:
$$Q_P + W'_P = \Delta U + P\Delta V$$

are

28

The full equation
reads:
$$\Delta H = \Delta U + P\Delta V$$

volume

28

✳ This circumstance that $P\Delta V$ under the specified conditions is a property of state permits
us to obtain a new thermodynamic function,
also a property of state, by deducting $-P\Delta V$
from ΔU. This operation yields ΔH, the
change in enthalpy. We can define the enthalpy
thus

$$H = U + PV$$

and for constant pressure

$$\Delta H = \underline{\hspace{1cm}} + P\Delta V$$

Here is the definition in words: The
change in enthalpy is the change in the internal energy of the system, minus the quantity
$-P\Delta V$, which is the energy stored in the
system owing to the change in ☐volume
☐pressure —i. e., we exclude the work
done on the system by its surroundings by a
volume change against a constant pressure.

29

✳ Parallel to our statement of the First Law,

$$\Delta U = Q + W$$

using the result of Item 27, we can write
another equation:

$$\Delta H = Q_P + W'_P$$

Thus we see that the relationship of W to
ΔU is paralleled by that of W'_P to $\underline{\hspace{1cm}}$.

✱ To help us understand the usefulness of the enthalpy, let us suppose that a process takes place at constant pressure without any useful work being done; i. e., $W' = 0$.

Since $W_P = W'_P - P\Delta V$,

$$\Delta U = Q_P - \underline{\hspace{2cm}}$$

To determine the change in energy, this equation tells us we must measure not only the heat exchanged but also the change in _____. This latter change is not always easily determined.

We greatly simplify matters by neglecting the work done as a result of this volume change in our new function of state, the enthalpy. Accordingly, in the absence of any net useful work done (i. e., when $W' = 0$),

$$\Delta H = Q_P$$

That is, under these conditions, the change in enthalpy corresponds to the heat exchanged at constant pressure. For this reason, reactions with positive ΔH are called *endothermic* and those with negative ΔH are called *exo*_____ (complete the word).

ΔH

30

31

The full equation
reads:

$$\varDelta U = Q_P - P\varDelta V$$

volume

The full word:
exothermic

✱ We have seen that the difference between $\varDelta H$ and $\varDelta U$ at constant pressure is _____ . Suppose we observe that in a certain reaction not only the pressure but also the volume remains constant. Such is the case to a close approximation for many biological reactions. Would the difference between $\varDelta H$ and $\varDelta U$ disappear under these conditions? _____ .

   Consider this example: When glucose is burned completely to carbon dioxide and water,

$$C_6H_{12}O_6 + 6O_2 \rightarrow 6CO_2 + 6H_2O$$

673,000 calories of heat are liberated per mole of glucose oxidized at 25° C. Hence, this reaction is ☐endothermic ☐exothermic. Since the CO_2 formed is equal mole for mole to the oxygen consumed, the change in volume is negligible. Noting that $\varDelta H = -673,000$ cal/mole, what is the value for $\varDelta U$ at 25° C?

_____ .

32

✳ If we were now to feed the glucose to a culture of bacteria, and to observe that only 400,000 cal/mole of glucose used were evolved while the growing bacteria converted the glucose completely to CO_2 and H_2O, which one of the following explanations could be accepted? The oxidation has yielded less heat

☐ 1. because about 40 per cent of the energy available from the oxidation of glucose has been stored as chemical energy.

☐ 2. because the glucose on burning raised the temperature. The heat removed in cooling the system to the original temperature of 25° C had then to be included in ΔH.

33

✳ To summarize this section, indicate which of the following statements gives rise to the First Law of Thermodynamics:

☐ 1. Careful measurement and summation of the energy of various kinds and origins in a system shows that the same total amount is always present at a given state.

☐ 2. Careful measurement of the heat and work exchanges of a system shows that the change in energy is always the same in going from one state to another, regardless of the pathway followed.

31

$P\Delta V$

Yes*

☑exothermic

−673,000 cal/mole
(since $\Delta U = \Delta H$ under the stated conditions)

32

☑1. because about 40 per cent of the chemical energy has been stored...
(Remember that ΔU and ΔH depend only on the initial and final states of the system, and not on the pathway followed.)

---

*This conclusion suggests that we could for biological purposes simplify our treatment by dispensing with the enthalpy, using the energy instead. Although you will usually not need to pay attention to the difference between ΔH and ΔU, you will see shortly that the *Gibbs free energy* is defined in terms of ΔH, not ΔU. Furthermore, values for ΔH are more often recorded than those for ΔU. Hence, we cannot dispense with a consideration of the difference in their definitions.

33

☐ 1. Careful measurement and summation of the energy...

(It is usually impossible to make direct measurement of various kinds of energy.)

☑ 2. Careful measurement of the heat and work exchanges...

THE SECOND LAW OF THERMODYNAMICS: FREE ENERGY, ENTROPY AND DISORDER

The Conversion of Heat Into Work

34

✳ The First Law fails to answer two questions about natural processes:

In which direction will a reaction go spontaneously?

How much work can we obtain from a reaction?

In the following 14 items we will use the Second Law of Thermodynamics to develop the means to answer these two important questions for the case of reactions occurring at constant temperature, the condition which applies to most biological processes. The student is urged to work through them especially carefully, because these are perhaps the most fundamental and at the same time the most conceptually difficult items of this program.

We can see the need for an additional principle by noting the following events:

ice $(+ 0.1^{\circ} C) \rightarrow$ water $(+ 0.1^{\circ} C)$,

$$\Delta U \simeq \Delta H = + 1437.2 \text{ cal/mole}$$

water $(- 0.1^{\circ} C) \rightarrow$ ice $(- 0.1^{\circ} C)$,

$$\Delta U \simeq \Delta H = - 1435.4 \text{ cal/mole}$$

(In this example, of course, the enthalpy change is just the heat of fusion.)

In the first of these, energy is absorbed and we can see that the process is ☑endothermic ☐exothermic; in the second, energy is ☐absorbed ☑given off. From everyday experience ☐the first is ☐the second is ☑both are process(es) that can actually occur without an external force. Such processes we have called *spontaneous* (or natural) processes.

34

endothermic

given off

both are

35

✱ Hence, the sign of the energy change ☑ reveals ☐ has failed to reveal in which direction the processes will go spontaneously. Moreover, nothing in the First Law implies any limit to the amount of work that can be obtained from a change of state, providing only that the total energy must be conserved. Thus, either of the equations

$$\Delta U = Q + W$$

or

$$\Delta H = Q_P + W'_P$$

suggests that if we transfer heat equal to ΔU or ΔH into a system we can achieve the desired change of state without doing any work at all; or if we put even more heat into the system we can get from it an amount of work equal to the excess over the energy change of the system. We know from experience (as already noted in Item 15) that this ☐ is ☐ is not uniformly true.

✳ It is the *Second Law of Thermodynamics* that formally states the conclusion of that experience. The Second Law has been stated in a number of ways, although these can all be shown to be equivalent. We will consider first the historic statement of Kelvin and Planck:

"It is impossible to convert heat into work by any process which at its conclusion has produced no other changes in the system or its surroundings."

In other words, even though the First Law suggests that different forms of energy are interconvertible, the Second Law puts some restrictions on this interconversion. Heat and work are not completely equivalent, and, in fact, ☐heat ☐work is a less generally useful form of energy.

As is the case for the First Law, the statement of the Second Law ☐can ☐cannot be proved mathematically. Conclusions derived from the statement are, however, in agreement with experimental observations.

has failed to reveal

is not

36

heat

cannot (Item 15)

37

No

37

✷ To see the usefulness of the Second Law, let us apply it to a particular case, that of processes occurring at constant temperature.

For these we may narrow the statement of the preceding item:

"It is impossible to remove heat from a system and to convert it completely into work by a cyclic, isothermal process."

Note that cycles can be devised that convert heat into work, but only with a net transfer of heat from a system at one temperature to a second system at a lower temperature. Can such a process be considered isothermal? _____.

38

✷ Organisms present essentially isothermal conditions within themselves. Ordinarily they live either at the same or at a higher temperature than their environment. Under such conditions, can organisms absorb heat from their environment and convert it into work? _____. Because of these circumstances we shall be concerned for the remainder of our treatment of thermodynamics with the determination of the work obtained in or required for isothermal processes.

✱ We must focus our attention on *work* because the Second Law tells us that if work can be obtained in one phase of an isothermal cycle (say the oxidation of glucose to CO_2 and H_2O at 37°C) *at least as much work* must be done on the system to return it to its original state.

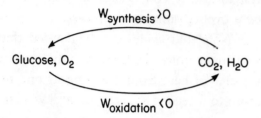

Note, however, that neither of our earlier statements of the Second Law (Items 36 and 37) puts any restriction on the conversion of *work* into *heat*. For example, if the restoration of the system to its original state is made inefficiently, a large excess of work may be required, and of course in such cases excess _____ will be produced.

No

39

heat

40

✱ We can restate the requirement of the Second Law for a cyclic process occurring within a system at constant temperature, first in words and then by an equation.

Stated in words: the work done by a system during a change in state can be equal to but it cannot be ☐more ☐less than the work required to restore the system to its original condition.

Stated as an equation, remembering that W represents work done on the system, and that

$$W_{net} = W_{forward} + W_{restoration}$$

(check one):

☐ 1. $W_{net} \leq 0$ (read $\leq$ "less than or equal to")

☐ 2. $W_{net} = 0$
☐ 3. $W_{net} \geq 0$ (read $\geq$ "greater than or equal to")

✱ We will now assert that the Second Law requires that there is a *maximal* amount of work that can be obtained from an isothermal process, such as the oxidative metabolism of glucose.

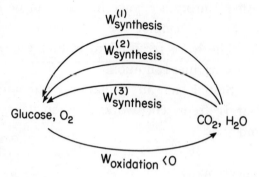

To prove this assertion we may note, as in this diagram, that there may be several isothermal paths by which we can restore the system to its original condition. Since the system can do work in the initial oxidation process, we must of course do some work on the system to restore it, no matter which pathway we actually choose. Theoretically, if enough pathways are tried we will find a limiting minimal value for the work required for synthesis. This amount must also be the ☐minimum   ☐maximum   that can be obtained *from* the forward (oxidative) process, independent of the actual pathway chosen, because if more could be obtained, we could devise an isothermal cycle for which $W_{net} < 0$ in violation of the Second Law.

more

☑3. $W_{net} \geq 0$

(This mathematical method of summarizing a situation may require special attention if you are not familiar with it.)

41

42

maximum

✳ Although the actual amount of work required for, or produced by, a given isothermal change depends on the path chosen, the above analysis indicates that a certain minimal amount is required, or a certain maximal amount can be produced, which depends only on the initial and final states of the system. We therefore find it useful to introduce a new function, the *free energy, G,* whose value depends only on the state of the system. This function measures the minimal useful work required for an isothermal process at constant temperature:

$$\Delta G = W_{min,T,P} - (-P\Delta V)$$

or

$$\Delta G = W'_{min,T,P}$$

We restrict ourselves here to constant temperature and pressure because these are the conditions one deals with in the biological context, and indeed for most chemical reactions.* We have used W' because we are interested in work other than that required for a change in _____, as discussed in Item 27.

---

*You may well encounter in textbooks a companion function to the *free energy,* namely the *work content* (A). It can be defined simply as $\Delta A = W_{min,T}$. In certain nonbiological contexts, where the temperature and the *volume* are constant, it may be preferred to G. The existence of this function has led to the choice of the symbol G rather than F for the free energy. Unfortunately, F has been used also in place of A, which is sometimes called the *Helmholtz free energy.* To avoid confusion, the symbol G has come to be widely preferred for the quantity which we have called and shall continue to call simply the *free energy,* which may also be called the *Gibbs free energy.*

42 A

✱   Recalling again that W always refers to the work done *on* the system, indicate the meaning of a negative value of ΔG for a given isothermal process.

☐ 1. This means that the system can do work on the surroundings.

☐ 2. This means that work must be done on the system by the surroundings during the change.

The value of $-\Delta G$ therefore tells us the ☐maximal   ☐minimal   work the system can do. This statement answers the second of the two questions we asked at the beginning of this section in Item 34, "How much work can we obtain from a given reaction?"

Reversible and Irreversible Processes
43

✱ The free energy will permit us to answer also the first of the two questions of Item 34, "In which direction will a reaction go spontaneously?"

For this purpose, as well as for the value of the distinction for its own sake, it will be

---

42

volume

---

42 A

☑1. This means that the system can do work on the surroundings.

maximal

useful first to distinguish between *reversible* and *irreversible* processes. *Reversibility* is another of those thermodynamic terms that must be defined in a precise way:

A reversible process is one that occurs in such a way that *both the system and its surroundings* can be returned to their original states.

This definition means that a process is reversible only if the work actually produced by the system during the process is sufficient to restore the system to its original condition. Note that the definition does not require us to reverse exactly the original pathway, or even to restore the system at all. It only requires that the work produced by the process must be sufficient to produce the restoration by a suitable pathway.

Consider this example: *ATP* serves in the living cell to couple two amino acids by a peptide bond, the *ATP* being broken down to *AMP* and 2 moles of inorganic phosphate as a result of the process. No chemical work is done by the *ATP* except formation of the peptide bond, which requires about 3500 cal/mole. The cell can of course resynthesize the *ATP* from its breakdown products, but to do so requires at least 14,600 cal/mole. Therefore we may say by our definition above that the hydrolysis of *ATP* in peptide synthesis is a(n) ☐reversible ☐irreversible reaction.

44

✳ Any process that occurs without meeting the above criterion we consider to be an irreversible process; we may say that it occurs along an irreversible pathway. Experience has shown us that most real processes occur without optimal utilization of the available work. Therefore, most processes that actually occur are ☐reversible ☐irreversible.

43

irreversible (Even though we can restore the system to its original condition, the surroundings in the cell must do more work to remanufacture the *ATP* than was obtained during the hydrolysis. Therefore it is impossible to restore the surroundings to the original condition.

45

✳ Recall from Item 41 that the *maximal* work a system can do *on its surroundings* in an isothermal process is equal to the ☐minimal ☐maximal work that must be done *on the system* to restore it to its original state. This equivalence is the criterion we have just shown to be necessary for a process to be _____ . Therefore, if we want to obtain the maximal work from a system during a given change of state, or to do the minimal work on a system necessary to achieve that change of state, we must select a (n) ☐reversible ☐irreversible pathway.

44

irreversible

45

minimal

reversible

reversible

46

✳ We can therefore talk about the "reversible work" done on a system: it is the work done during a reversible change. Since a pathway must be reversible for the minimal work to be done on a system during a given change, we can write

$$W'_{min, T, P} = W'_{rev, T, P}$$

Remembering then that W always refers to the work done *on* a system and that the reversible work is the *minimal* work, place one of the symbols, $=$, $>$ or $<$, in the box of this expression:

$$W'_{rev, T, P} \ \square \ W'_{irrev, T, P}$$

This expression says that to effect a change by a reversible pathway always requires ☐more ☐less work than by an irreversible pathway.

✷ The expression just obtained can also be used when the system is capable of doing work. In this case, recall from Item 20 that the work done *on the surroundings* is equal to the negative of the work done *on the system*. Thus, if the work done *on the system* is less than zero, (check one)

☐ 1. the system is doing work on the sur-roundings.

☐ 2. the surroundings are doing work on the system.

One of the rules for the manipulation of inequalities says that if you multiply both sides of the inequality by −1, you change the direction of the inequality, thus

$$- W'_{rev, T, P} > - W'_{irrev, T, P}$$

This result tells us that the useful work a system can do *on its surroundings* in a reversible isothermal process is always ☐less than ☐greater than the work done by the system in an irreversible process between the same two states. Thus, any real process produces ☐more ☐less work than would be available under optimal (reversible) conditions. This is an inescapable conclusion from the Second Law, and is completely consistent with our experience.

The complete equa-tion:
$$W'_{rev, T, P} \leq W'_{irrev, T, P}$$

less

47

☑1. The system is doing work on...

greater than

less

48

* We defined the free energy change in Item 42 as follows:

$$\Delta G = W'_{min, T, P}$$

The development of Item 46 permits us also to say

$$\Delta G = W'_{rev, T, P}$$

and also

$$\Delta G < W'_{irrev, T, P}$$

Combining these two, we have

$$\Delta G \leq W'_{T, P}$$

Here the equality applies to the condition of _____. The inequality applies to _____.

    Note that according to the Second Law there is no isothermal process occurring at constant pressure for which this expression does not hold. A process is either reversible or irreversible. There is no third alternative.

✷ Recall that if $\Delta G > 0$, then $W'_{T,P} > 0$; that is, the system will require an input of work for the change to occur. Conversely, if $\Delta G < 0$, the change can occur without the input of work; that is, it can take place *spontaneously*, and with proper arrangements the system can do useful work on the surroundings as the change goes on.

If a system is isolated so that it can do no work and have no work done on it, then $W' = 0$. In this case for a change in the system at constant temperature and pressure, we can rewrite the last equation of Item 48 (check the correct answer).

☐1. $\Delta G = 0$
☐2. $\Delta G \leq 0$
☐3. $\Delta G \geq 0$

reversibility

irreversibility

☐1. $\Delta G = 0$

(Only for the con-
dition of reversi-
bility.)

☑2. $\Delta G \leq 0$

(The equality apply-
ing for reversible
and the inequality
for irreversible
changes.)

☐3. $\Delta G \geq 0$

(If the system is to
gain free energy,
work must be done
on it.)

✳ The selected equation means that if an isolated system is not at equilibrium, its free energy will tend spontaneously to ☐decrease ☐increase until it has reached a minimum, at which point a small change in the system (that is, one not large enough to move it out of equilibrium) can be made in either direction without requiring any external work, and hence without any free energy change. Hence at equilibrium, $\Delta G = 0$.

The conclusion that the free energy change must be negative for any real process occurring at constant temperature and pressure and that $\Delta G = 0$ at equilibrium is the most significant one we have reached in this program. To reach this concept we have used the Second Law to show that only part of the total energy of a system is available to do useful work. In this way we have established the contrast between:

(a) energy unavailable to do work

(b) energy that can do useful work

At the state of equilibrium of an isolated system ☐only the first of these is ☐only the second is ☐both are necessarily at a minimum.

51

* Recall that thermodynamics makes no predictions about the rates of processes. Furthermore, when we say that a reaction will proceed *spontaneously* we do not mean *rapidly*, we mean *without work being done on it.*

The converse of the generalization we just reached, namely that *spontaneous processes show negative values of* ΔG, might be proposed, that is, that a reaction which fails to proceed during a long period of observation must have a zero or positive ΔG. Can we accept that conclusion? ______.

50

decrease

only the second is

51

No

52

* The diagram shows why a certain reaction fails to occur unless a requisite amount of energy is supplied, for example by raising the temperature locally, perhaps by an electric spark. The free energy level of the reactants is represented by the horizontal mark at *B*, whereas the mark at *C* represents the free energy of the products. (The scale represents no zero point of free energy.)

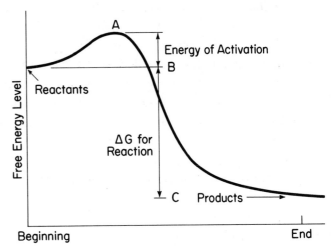

We can see that the overall reaction is ☐spontaneous ☐not spontaneous. Under ordinary conditions, however, the reaction must pass through the intermediate marked *A*, which ☐will also ☐may not be formed spontaneously.

If the *energy of activation* is large, external energy must be supplied initially to start the process, in which case the energy of activation plus the free energy change of the reaction will be released as the reaction proceeds; or else a catalyst must be added to make it possible for the reaction to take a course not requiring so large an energy of _____.

spontaneous

may not

activation

Entropy

53

✱ The preceding analysis does not fully define G because we limited ourselves to conditions of constant _____ and _____ . We could choose to develop a thermodynamic function directly from the Second Law, one that relates to the minimal work required in any process, without restricting ourselves to these conditions. The developers of thermodynamic theory were more concerned with heat engines, however, and therefore the function they chose to work with, namely the *entropy,* is defined in terms of heat exchange rather than work.

Although the entropy is historically the more basic concept, students find it more difficult to understand than the free energy, and it has more restricted usefulness for biochemical processes. We have therefore chosen to discuss the two functions in the order opposite to that which is usually followed, and as you will see in this program we have limited our treatment of biochemical systems to the free energy. The student may, therefore, if he prefers or is so directed, pass on to Item 73 and defer his study of the entropy to a later time.

We concluded in Item 50 that any system contains in addition to its useful energy a certain amount of energy _____ _____ in an isothermal process.

53

temperature,
  pressure
(in either order)
not available for
  doing work (or
  words to that
  effect)

54

Since we cannot measure directly the energy content of a system, the only way we can discover what portion of the energy is unavailable for doing work is to observe what happens during the transfer of energy to or from the system. Because a change of energy not productive of work will be represented by a transfer of heat, we are led to search for a measure of this "unavailable energy" in the _____ exchanges of the system.

54

heat

55

To say that the heat in a system is per se the unavailable energy would, however, be to assert that the heat absorbed or given off in going from one state to another is a definite quantity, independent of the pathway followed. Have we defined Q itself as one of the thermodynamic quantities that is independent of pathway? _____.

We must therefore search further to see how the heat exchanges of a system are related to its content of energy unavailable for work. Recall, from Items 41 and 42, that at constant temperature the *reversible* (i. e., minimal) work is independent of the path and therefore dependent only on the state of the system at the beginning and end of the specified change. Similarly, since the right hand side of the equation

No

$$Q_{rev,T} = \Delta U - W_{rev,T}$$

is independent of the path, the left hand side is also, and we may therefore conclude that the amount of heat exchanged in a *reversible, isothermal* process is ☐ dependent on the pathway chosen ☐ dependent only on the initial and final states of the system.

56

dependent only on
the initial and
final states. . .

57

Since $Q_{rev,T}$ is independent of the specific pathway, $Q_{rev,T}$ divided by the temperature at which the process occurs will also be independent of the path. By an analysis which is too complex to trace in this program, it can be shown that even though for nonisothermal processes the value of Q_{rev} observed depends on the path chosen, the quotient Q_{rev}/T is independent of the path when T is the temperature measured on the absolute (Kelvin) or ideal gas temperature scale. Therefore, Q_{rev}/T, like ΔU and ΔH, is a function only of the initial and final states of the system.

In this way, we come to define the *entropy*, S, as another thermodynamic function, as follows:

$$\Delta S = Q_{rev}/T^*$$

Have we said that Q_{irrev}/T is a function only of the initial and final states, as ΔU and ΔH are? _____.

Is the entropy a function whose value depends only on the state of the system, like the energy and enthalpy? _____.

---

*Students familair with calculus will see that to be more precise we might better write $\Delta S = \int_{A}^{B} dQ_{rev}/T$ for the change in entropy in going from state A to state B since, in general, the temperature also varies along the path. Because this integral is independent of the path, whereas the integral of Q_{rev} is not, $1/T$ is called an *integrating factor* for Q_{rev}. Note that just as was the case in our definition of the energy, U, we have established no zero value for the entropy, but have merely defined the entropy difference between two states. The Third Law of Thermodynamics, not considered in this program, does establish a zero point for entropy although not for energy. The reader is referred to a standard textbook of thermodynamics for a discussion of that subject.

We have merely inferred and not proved that the entropy is a function of state. The following example offers support for such an inference. (In studying this example, you should focus your attention only on the overall comparison of the values for the various terms, not on the details of the various pathways.)

If 1 mole of helium is carried from conditions of $T = 100°C$, $P = 2$ atm to $T = 25°C$, $P = 1$ atm by a variety of pathways, as listed below, the first four being reversible paths and the fifth irreversible, the following values are obtained for the work, heat, and Q/T for the transition(calculate the energy change for each case):

Pathway	W	Q	ΔU $(W + Q)$	Q/T*
	cal	cal	cal	(cal/K)
1. Expansion with $Q = 0$ until $P = 1$ atm, then T brought to 25°C.	−298	+74.5	_____	+0.264
2. Cooling at constant $P = 2$ atm until $T = 25°$ C, then P reduced to 1 atm at constant T.	−264	+39	_____	+0.263
3. Heating at constant P until final volume is reached, then cooling at constant V to 25°C, 1 atm pressure.	−443.8	+220	_____	+0.26
4. Cooling at constant V until $P = 0.5$ atm, then heating at constant P until final volume is reached; finally, T brought to 25°C at constant V.	−110	−113	_____	+0.26
5. Irreversible flow through a porous filter from $P = 2$ atm to $P = 1$ atm, followed by (reversibly) bringing the temperature to 25°C at constant P.	+148	−372	_____	−1.11

No

Yes

*Measured by taking the integral, $\int dQ/T$, over each path.

Thus, we see that only the following are independent of the path:
(check the appropriate box or boxes)

☐ 1. The work done on the system (W)

☐ 2. The heat absorbed by the system (Q)

☐ 3. The total energy change of the system (ΔU)

☐ 4. Q/T for any pathway

☐ 5· Q/T for any reversible pathway

$$\Delta U = -224, \ -225,$$
$$-224, \ -223$$
$$\text{and} \ -224$$

☐ 1. The work
done...

☐ 2. The heat
absorbed...

☑ 3. The total
energy change...

☐ 4. Q/T for any
pathway

☑ 5. Q/T for any
reversible
pathway (ΔS)

For irreversible pathways, Q_{irrev}/T is in general dependent on the path chosen and therefore is not a useful measure of the change in state of a system. If we want to discover the entropy change between two states, we have no choice but to determine Q/T along a(n) _____ pathway.

We can draw some conclusions, however, about whether the entropy change is *larger* or *smaller* than values that we may observe for Q_{irrev}/T for irreversible processes. (The student who wishes to avoid the derivation may skip to Item 62.)

In Item 47 from the Second Law we derived an inequality relating the reversible and irreversible useful work done *by* a system. A similar relationship holds for the total work as follows:

$$- W_{rev, T} > - W_{irrev, T}$$

We may now write the First Law for two special cases

$$\Delta U = Q_{rev, T} + W_{rev, T}$$
$$\Delta U = Q_{irrev, T} + W_{irrev, T}$$

It follows from these two equations that (supply one of the symbols, $=$, $>$ or $<$, in the box below):

$$\Delta U = Q_{rev, T} + W_{rev, T} \, \square \, Q_{irrev, T} + W_{irrev, T}$$

reversible

60

The full statement should read:

$$\Delta U = Q_{rev,\,T}$$
$$+ \, W_{rev,\,T}$$
$$\boxminus \, Q_{irrev,\,T}$$
$$+ \, W_{irrev,\,T}$$

(i.e., ΔU is independent of the pathway.)

61

By adding equal quantities to each side of an inequality, we preserve the inequality and do not change its direction. Therefore by adding the inequality and the final equation of the preceding items we obtain (again supply the appropriate symbols for equality or inequality):

$$Q_{rev,\,T} \,\Box\, Q_{irrev,\,T}$$

and at constant temperature,

$$\Delta S = Q_{rev,\,T}/T \,\Box\, Q_{irrev,\,T}/T$$

Hence if we were to measure Q/T under conditions of thermodynamic irreversibility we would $\Box$underestimate $\Box$overestimate the change in entropy.

Are the data in Item 58 consistent with this conclusion? _____ .

61

The full statements should read:

$$Q_{rev,\,T} \boxgeq Q_{irrev,\,T}$$

$$\Delta S = Q_{rev,\,T}/T$$
$$\boxgeq Q_{irrev,\,T}/T.$$

underestimate

Yes $(+ \, 0.260$
$$> \, - \, 1.11)$$

62

From the foregoing we may state that the change of entropy is either equal to or greater than Q/T; thus, we write

$$\Delta S \geq Q/T$$

where the stated equality holds for _____ pathways and the stated inequality for _____ pathways. We may take this expression as a mathematical statement of the Second Law.*

---

*Again, to be exact we should write $\Delta S \geq \int_{A}^{B} dQ/T$. Note that we have actually proved this inequality here only for isothermal processes. The more general result can be derived from our earlier verbal statement of the Second Law, but such a derivation is beyond the scope of this program.

63

A more commonly seen mathematical statement of this law can be reached by considering systems isolated from their surroundings so that no heat exchange can occur. Note that such systems need not be isolated systems because work can still be done *by* or *on* the system. Since for the case described, $Q = 0$,

$\Delta S = 0$ for _____ processes,

$\Delta S > 0$ for _____ processes.

62

reversible

irreversible

64

Note that the statements of Item 63 hold for any system *plus its environment*, even if the system is not thermally isolated from its surroundings. The statements ☐will therefore ☐will not, however, hold for such a nonisolated system by itself.

63

reversible

irreversible

64

will not, however,

65

The two mathematical statements of Item 63 indicate that if a thermally isolated system (or any system plus its environment) is changed in such a way that one does not obtain the maximal work available from the transformation, its content of an unavailable form of energy, as measured by the entropy, is increased. They also tell us that the entropy will tend ☐only to increase, never to decrease ☐sometimes to increase, sometimes to decrease during any *spontaneous* (irreversible) change in an isolated system. This tendency continues until the entropy reaches a ☐minimum ☐maximum, and we can say that the system has completely "run down," its energy having been maximally degraded in its ability to produce work.

Note that the two mathematical formulations of Item 63 can be applied conversely to determine whether a process is spontaneous, provided that we have an independent measure of the change in entropy. Consider the system, water and ice, in relation to its surroundings:*

	ΔS_{sys}	ΔS_{surr}	ΔS_{total}
		(calories/mole K)	
water (+0.1°) → ice (+0.1°)	−5.2613	+5.2595	−0.0018†
water (0.0°) → ice (0.0°)	−5.2581	+5.2581	0.0000
water (−0.1°) → ice (−0.1°)	−5.2549	+5.2567	+0.0018

From the values cited for ΔS_{total}, we may conclude that ice melts spontaneously at _____°, that water freezes spontaneously at _____°, and that at 0° the two forms are in equilibrium, that is, they can be interchanged ☐reversibly ☐irreversibly. We note also that ΔS_{sys} by itself ☐does ☐does not tell us the direction of spontaneous change because the system is not isolated.

only to increase,
never to decrease

maximum

*Assuming that the heat of fusion is absorbed by the surroundings at the temperature specified. These surroundings might, for example, be the fluid in a calorimeter in which the ice-water system is held.
†We should point out a fundamental property of all thermodynamic functions that depend on the state of the system. For a pathway from B to A, the change in value of the function will be equal but of opposite sign to the change for a path from A to B. Hence, for the transition, ice (+ 0.1°) → water (+ 0.1°), ΔS_{total} = + 0.0018 cal/mole K.

66

+ 0.1 °C

− 0.1 °C

reversibly (because
$\Delta S_{total} = 0$)

does not

67

The entropy as defined here is a mathematical construct which, as we have seen, has some useful properties. Thermodynamics really does not provide any means for our gaining a better understanding of what the entropy is, but by relating observed entropy changes to some of the molecular properties of the system we can gain some insight into its meaning. (The situation really is no different for energy: we can really understand what energy is only by reference to the molecular properties of the system, and not by any thermodynamic definition.)

The entropy is often spoken of as a measure of disorder, so that the tendency of the entropy to increase represents the tendency of randomness to replace order and of improbable arrangements to shift toward more probable ones. The order and randomness we refer to may be of various kinds. For example, in the case just discussed, the crystallization of water calls for the molecules to assume an ordered arrangement in space. That being the case, we should expect the entropy of ice tabulated in Item 66 to be ☐higher ☐lower than that of water at all three temperatures recorded. The tabulation confirms that this is so.

68

At first thought, you may protest, why does water ever freeze at all, when to do so its entropy must decrease, and when we maintain that in general the entropy instead tends only to ☐decrease ☐increase? Since the ice-water system is not isolated from its environment, this requirement that the entropy tends only to increase must apply to the *total entropy*, that of the system plus its _____, as shown in the right-hand column of the table of Item 66.

67

lower (note column headed ΔS_{sys})

69

For the ice-water system alone, heat must be given off for freezing to occur, hence the energy content, U(or the enthalpy, H), for the system will ☐decrease ☐increase during freezing, as indeed we noted in Item 34. When we summate Q_{rev}/T for the surroundings and the entropy change for the water-ice system itself, we obtain the *total entropy change*, which is the information we need to predict in which direction the process will go, that of freezing or thawing. That is, the process can occur spontaneously if ΔS for the system plus its surroundings is ☐positive ☐negative.

68

increase

surroundings (environment)
(See Items 63–65)

69

decrease

positive

70

It is sometimes claimed that living organisms violate the Second Law of Thermodynamics, because they appear to become more ordered as the time proceeds. (Contrast an egg with an adult organism.) We must remember, however, that organisms are ☐ open ☐ closed systems. They receive food from their environment, and with the energy they extract from that food they do the work of building their orderly structures. Furthermore, the processes used are somewhat inefficient, so that heat is evolved and transferred to the environment. If we consider the organism and its environment together, we will see that the entropy of the total system is ☐ increased ☐ decreased.*

70

open

increased

71

From the foregoing, we see that the direction in which a change in a system will proceed can be determined by the sign on (choose the correct statement or statements):

☐ 1. ΔU for the system

☐ 2. ΔH for the system

☐ 3. ΔS for the system, if the system is isolated from its surroundings

☐ 4. ΔS_{total}, for the system plus its surroundings

☐ 5. ΔG for the system, when the change occurs at constant temperature and pressure

*The circumstance that the entropy always tends to increase in real processes may be said to reveal the direction of time, and to refute the contentions that it is a psychological illusion that time moves forward rather than backward, and that cause and effect are really different. That is, the direction of increasing entropy may be said to be the *forward* direction for time. See H. F. Blum, *Time's Arrow and Evolution* (Princeton University Press, Princeton, N.J., 1951).

72

71

We have seen that we can use either ΔG or ΔS to determine whether a reaction will proceed spontaneously or not. Note an advantage of ΔG over ΔS for that purpose. We saw in Items 63 and 64 that either of two provisos had to be included if ΔS were to serve for that prediction: Either the system must be isolated from its surroundings, or else we must measure the entropy of the system plus its surroundings, not that of the system alone. In developing the relation, $\Delta G \leq 0$, for a reaction that proceeds spontaneously, did we specify that no heat must be released or taken up? _____ .

☐ 1. ⎫ (Remember
☐ 2. ⎭ that the First
Law fails to
predict the
direction.)
☑ 3. (but only in
this specific
case)
☑ 4.
☑ 5.

72

No (Therefore we can apply this criterion to systems that are not isolated as long as they are maintained at constant temperature and pressure.)

The Complete Definition of Free Energy

73

* We can now resolve the problem of a satisfactory definition of the free energy noted in Item 53. We first use our definition of the entropy change to determine just how much of the energy of a system represented by ΔE or ΔH is usable for performing work. Begin by solving the equation

$$\Delta S = Q_{rev,\,T}/T$$

for $Q_{rev,\,T}$ as follows:

_____

73

$$Q_{rev,\,T} = T\Delta S$$

74

* You will recall from Item 29 that from the First Law and from the definition of enthalpy, we obtained an equation expressing the relationship between W'_P and ΔH,

$$\Delta H = \underline{\hspace{1cm}} + W'_P$$

We can rephrase this equation for the case of a reversible change at constant temperature and pressure. After rearranging terms, we obtain

$$W'_{rev,\,T,\,P} = \underline{\hspace{2cm}} - Q_{P,\,T,\,rev}$$

75

✳ In the latter equation, substitute for $Q_{rev, T}$ the equivalent value you obtained in Item 73:

$$W'_{rev, T, P} = \Delta H - \underline{\hspace{3cm}}$$

76

✳ In Item 42 we introduced the term ΔG for the minimal (or *reversible*) work required to effect a change in a system, specifying isothermal conditions in our provisional definition. In agreement with the statement of the preceding item, namely,

$$W'_{rev, T, P} = \Delta H - T \Delta S$$

we are finally able to make the more adequate definition of free energy:*

$$G = H - TS$$

For constant temperature we can write

$$\Delta G = \underline{\hspace{3cm}}$$

Here we have our standard and universal definitions of the free energy and the change in free energy.

*To avoid possible confusion in any other reading you may do, note again that there is a companion thermodynamic function, the *work content*, which has a companion set of definitions to those for G:
$A = U - TS$ (or at constant temperature, $\Delta A = \Delta U - T \Delta S$);
$\Delta A = W_{rev, T}$

74

The complete equations:
$$\Delta H = Q_P + W'_P$$
$$W'_{rev, P, T} = \Delta H - Q_{P, T, rev}$$
(Question:
Why is it not necessary to make the specification ΔH_{rev}?)

75

The complete equation:
$$W'_{rev, T, P} = \Delta H - T \Delta S$$

76

The complete equation:

$$\Delta G = \Delta H - T \Delta S$$

77

✳ One way we can paraphrase this equation in words is by saying that the gain in useful work in a system as a result of a change is less than one would suppose from its gain in energy or enthalpy by an amount measured by the gain in _____ .

77

entropy

78

✳ From the first and third equations of Item 76 we can derive the relation between ΔG and W'_{rev} at constant temperature and pressure,

$$\Delta G = \underline{\hspace{3cm}}$$

78

The complete equation:

$$\Delta G = W'_{rev, T, P}$$

79

✳ Accordingly, and consistent with our original definition in Item 42, ΔG indicates the minimal ☐total ☐useful energy a system requires in undergoing a specified change, under conditions of constant temperature and ☐pressure ☐volume, these being the conditions most generally applicable in the biological context.

80

✱ We should now consider again the example of the freezing of water at $+0.1°$, $0.0°$ and $-0.1°$. When we combine the data of Items 34 and 66 (noting that the volume change is so small that we can set $\Delta H = \Delta U$), we obtain for that transition the following thermodynamic quantities in calories per mole (complete the table):

T	ΔH	$T\Delta S$	$\Delta H - T\Delta S$	ΔG
$+0.1°C$	-1437.2	$273.26\ (-5.2613)$	$-1437.2 +1437.7$	____
$0.0°C$	-1436.3	$273.16\ (-5.2581)$	$-1436.3 +1436.3$	____
$-0.1°C$	-1435.4	$273.06\ (-5.2549)$	$-1435.4 +1434.9$	____

Do the results correspond to common knowledge as to spontaneity in the freezing of water and the melting of ice? _____.

Note, as discussed in Item 72, that in obtaining this result we have had to consider ☐ the system alone ☐ the system plus surroundings.

81

✱ A saturated solution by definition is in equilibrium with a crystalline form of the solute. State numerically the free energy change for the following process:

glucose (saturated solution) →
glucose (crystal)

$\Delta G =$ _____

[At this point you may wish to try Summary Items 264–272 inclusive and Objective Examination Items 1–21 and 43–46 inclusive, if you suspect that a restudy of the section on the free energy may be desirable before proceeding.]

79

useful

pressure

80

T	ΔG
$+0.1\ °C$	$+0.5$
$0.0\ °C$	0.0
$-0.1\ °C$	-0.5

Yes

the system alone

81

Zero

82

is spontaneous (Remember, we must turn to kinetics for consideration of rates of processes.)

CHEMICAL REACTIONS

Dependence of ΔG on Concentration: The Chemical Potential

82

✱ The same concepts we just applied above to two physical processes, the freezing of water and the growth and dissolution of crystals, apply to chemical reactions. The following reaction

$$2H_2(1 \text{ atm}) + O_2(1 \text{ atm}) \rightarrow 2H_2O(\text{gas, 1 atm})$$
$$\Delta G = -54.64 \text{ kcal/mole}$$

☐ is spontaneous and necessarily rapid ☐ requires work.

☐ is spontaneous ☐ is at equilibrium

83

✱ Consider this equation for glucose synthesis:

$$6CO_2(0.05 \text{ atm}) + 6H_2O \text{ (liquid)} \rightarrow$$
$$C_6H_{12}O_6(0.01 \text{ } M) + 6O_2(0.2 \text{ atm})$$

The value of ΔG is found to be $+688.68$ kcal/mole. Accordingly the reaction will ☐ tend to occur spontaneously ☐ require external work.

84

83

* We will restate the key concept in the context of chemical reactions occurring at constant temperature and pressure: To determine whether or not a reaction will proceed spontaneously, and how much useful energy we can get from it, we need to determine the ☐total energy change ☐free energy change ☐heat evolved.

require external work

  The remainder of this program is concerned with how we can determine this quantity for a variety of biological processes and then use it in analyzing them.

84

free energy change

85

free energy

85

✱ Chemical reactions lead to changes in concentrations both of reactants and of products. Our next concern will be to find a general way to describe how the free energy of a system changes as the concentration of each component changes. Then, if we can determine ΔG for one set of concentrations, we will be able to find ΔG for any other set. For this purpose we will first define a quantity called the *chemical potential*.

[Students following a severely abbreviated path through this program, including omission of the last section of the program, *Membrane Equilibria,* could skip to Item 108 at this point, thereby accepting without study the equation for the change in the free energy resulting from a chemical reaction.]

The chemical potential of component A, which we will designate μ_A, (μ being the Greek letter *mu*) measures the change in the free energy of the system for a change of 1 mole in the amount of A present, all other components being kept constant. That is, if n_A is the number of moles of A present, then when $\Delta n_A = 1$, other components kept constant, the change in the _____ will give us the value of μ_A.

86

✱ In the reaction, $A \to B$, should we measure the chemical potential of A by observing how much the free energy of a system is changed when 1 mole of A is converted to B? _____.

87

✻ Even though we define the chemical potential as the change in the free energy produced by adding or removing 1 mole of A, can we in practice add or remove that much of any component without changing the concentrations of the other components? _____. Therefore, it would be better to define μ_A in the language of calculus.

The student who has not studied calculus may wish to skip the next three items, going directly to Item 91.

88

The student who has studied calculus will recognize that under this approach we specify how much the free energy changes per infinitesimal changes in the amount of A. Hence, the chemical _____ of A is the derivative of G with respect to n_A. This derivative is actually a *partial derivative*, because for the present we are interested in the change of G ☐only with respect to one ☐with respect to all of the variables that will influence G.

89

While a regular derivative is written dG/dn_A, a partial derivative is written $\partial G/\partial n_A$.

In the equation

$$\mu_A = (\partial G/\partial n_A)_{P, T, n_B, n_C} \cdots$$

subscripts have been added to indicate that other independent variables have been kept constant, namely

(1) _____ (2) _____
(3) _____ .

86

No (A part of the free energy change would arise from the increase by one mole in the amount of B present.)

87

No

88

potential

only with respect to one.

89

temperature, pres-
sure, the quantit-
ies of all other
components
(any order)

90

The convenience of this definition of the
_____ potential will be seen when we
assemble the expression for the total change
in the free energy of the system:

$$\Delta G_{T,P} = (\partial G/\partial n_A)_{T,P,n_B,n_C} \ldots \Delta n_A$$
$$+ (\partial G/\partial n_B)_{T,P,n_A,n_C} \ldots \Delta n_B \ldots$$

or,

$$\Delta G_{T,P} = \mu_A \Delta n_A + \underline{\hspace{2cm}} + \ldots$$

This equation permits us to consider at once
the changes in all components occurring at
the same time.

✻ Whether we proceed from the symbolism of calculus of the preceding three items, or from the words of Item 85, we come to the same fundamental statement of the total change of the free energy in a reaction,

$$A + B \rightarrow C + D$$

proceeding at constant temperature and pressure:

$$\Delta G_{T,P} = \mu_A \Delta n_A + \mu_B \Delta n_B + \mu_C \Delta n_C + \mu_D \Delta n_D$$

Thus, we have defined the change in the free energy of the system in terms of its component parts.*

In this expression the numerical values of Δn_A and Δn_B will be equal to those of Δn_C and Δn_D and of the ☐same ☐opposite sign.

chemical

$\mu_B \Delta n_B$

---

*Note that for complete consistency we should write the differentials dG, dn_A... instead of ΔG, Δn_A ... Even though we have not done so here, it is important that μ_A, μ_B. . . remain essentially constant during the change if these expressions are to determine accurately the actual free energy change.

91

opposite

92

The complete equa-
tion:
$$\Delta G_{T,P,n_B} \cdots = \mu_1 \Delta n_1 + \mu_2 \Delta n_2$$

92

✳ Consider the following example: Two phases are separated by an interface. This might be a gas-liquid interface, an interface between two immiscible liquids, or some kind of a barrier between two aqueous solutions. In biology we frequently use the term *membrane* only for the latter case; but from the thermodynamic point of view we prefer to use the term *membrane* for any specified interface. We will suppose that the membrane is permeable to component *A*.

Let μ_1 be the chemical potential of *A* on one side of the interface, and μ_2, that on the other side. Our purpose will be to determine from the values of μ_1 and μ_2 whether a component will migrate from one phase to the other, and in which direction. The free energy change occurring in the system when net movement of *A* occurs across the interface will be given by this equation:

$$\Delta G_{T,P,n_B} \cdots = \mu_1 \Delta n_1 + \underline{\qquad\qquad}$$

93

✳ Since the system is *closed*, the total supply of *A* will be conserved; hence $\Delta n_1 = -\Delta n_2$. Therefore we can simplify the above expression as follows:

$$\Delta G_{T,P,n_B} \cdots = (\mu_1 - \underline{\qquad}) \, \Delta n_1$$

94

✱ This quantity of free energy is the work required to transport Δn_1 moles of A from phase 2 to phase 1.

We have previously drawn the fundamental conclusion that at equilibrium ΔG must equal ☐more than zero ☐less than zero ☐zero. Hence, at equilibrium,

$$\mu_1 = \mu_2$$

(Does this statement imply that at equilibrium our component will reach the same *concentration* in the two phases? _____.)

95

✱ This simple equation says that the chemical potential of any component at an equilibrium of distribution is constant across a phase boundary. If μ_1 is greater than μ_2, the direction of migration that will cause a loss of free energy is ☐from phase 1 to phase 2 ☐from phase 2 to phase 1. Will this be the direction in which spontaneous net migration will occur? _____ .

93

The complete equation:

$$\Delta G_{T,P,n_B}\cdots = (\mu_1 - \mu_2)\, \Delta n_1$$

94

zero

No (By no means! Consider that the interface in question may separate two dissimilar liquids, e. g., water and ether, and that the numerical relationship between μ and concentration will be different in the two phases.)

95

from phase 1 to phase 2 (Δn_1 is negative.)

Yes

96

✶ This concept is fundamental to the study of biological transport. When we observe that a substance instead migrates into a region where its chemical potential is higher than that in the phase from which it originates, we may say that ☐ a spontaneous movement is taking place ☐ work is required. We call such a process an *active transport*.

96

work is required

97

✶ To reach the conclusion that the chemical potential of a component at an equilibrium of distribution is constant across a membrane, did we have to stipulate anything about the distribution of other components between the two phases? _____. Does the equation

$$\mu_1 = \mu_2$$

hold for each component at equilibrium, in a multicomponent system? _____.

✽ Consider once more the chemical reaction, $A + B \rightarrow C + D$.

Again we may note that the conservation principle applies; for each molecule of A used up, a molecule of B also disappears, and one each of C and D appears. Hence, as we noted in Item 91, we may relate the changes in the quantities of these components as follows,

$$- \Delta n_A = - \Delta n_B = \Delta n_C = \Delta n_D$$

to reach a simple expression for the free energy change,

$$\Delta G_{T,P} = \{(\mu_C + \mu_D) - (\underline{\hspace{1cm}})\} \Delta n_D$$

In words, we can say that the free energy change produced by the reaction is the sum of the chemical potentials of the products, minus the _____ of the _____, times the number of moles of either product formed.

No (See the definition of chemical potential in Item 85.)

Yes

98

$\mu_A + \mu_B$

sum of the chemical
potentials

reactants

99

✳ For the more general reaction,

$$aA + bB \rightarrow eE + fF$$

(where a, b, e and f are the number of each component required to balance the equation) we can retain the proper stoichiometry by noting that when

$$\Delta n_A = -a$$

then $\qquad \Delta n_B = -b$

$$\Delta n_E = +e$$

and $\qquad \Delta n_F = +f$

Thus $\quad \Delta G = (e\mu_E + f\mu_F) - (a\mu_A + b\mu_B)$

and at equilibrium, $\Delta G = 0$; thus

$$e\mu_E + f\mu_F = \underline{\qquad\qquad}$$

99

$a\mu_A + b\mu_B$

100

✳ It is important to realize that ΔG is an extensive quantity; that is, the actual number of moles of each substance that react will affect its value. Frequently, however, in order that comparisons can be more easily made, free energy changes are stated *per mole of reaction, as the equation has been written,* as in the case above, for example, where a moles of A and b moles of B react, etc.

We note that if $a/2$ moles of A, etc., react, as long as the system remains at equilibrium, ΔG ☐will ☐will not equal zero.

✳ We have not yet said anything about the character of the dependence of μ on concentration. Experimentally, solutes at very low concentrations have been observed to follow this equation:

$$\mu_A = \mu_A^0 + RT \ln [A]$$

where $[A]$ is the molar concentration of A.

The quantity, μ_A^0, equals μ_A at a 1 M concentration. Its value is of course independent of concentration, although it does depend on temperature and pressure. *One molar* is therefore known as the *standard state* of A. R is the gas constant, 1.99 cal/mole K; T is the absolute temperature; and $\ln$ designates the logarithm to the base e. We can write this equation in several ways*:

$$\mu_A = \mu_A^0 + 2.303RT \log [A]$$
$$\mu_A = \mu_A^0 + 4.576T \ \log [A]$$
$$\mu_A = \mu_A^0 + \underline{\quad\quad} \log [A] \text{ at } 25 \ °C \ (298 \ K)$$

Since R is expressed as 1.99 cal/mole K, the value of μ_A will be obtained in calories per mole.

will

---

*See the page facing the back cover for values of useful constants and conversion factors which can be used in solving various problems in this program. It should also be noted that the numerical value of R will differ depending on the units used to express the energy (calories, joules, liter-atmospheres, etc.).

101

1364.2 cal/mole
(5707.8 joules/
mole)

102

✱ This relation between μ_A and $[A]$ holds exactly only for very dilute solutions, where the laws of ideal solutions are closely followed. For ordinary solutions, it is only approximately correct, so that we ought to write

$$\mu_A \cong \mu_A^0 + RT \, ln \, [A]$$

For precision we must introduce the *activity*, a. We will define a so that it becomes equal to the concentration at infinite dilution, and so that it satisfies this equation

$$\mu_A = \mu_A^0 + RT \, ln \, a_A$$

From this equation, you can see that the standard state of A has been defined here so that $\mu_A = \mu_A^0$ at unit ☐activity ☐concentration.

---

*It is of course possible to define the activity in a different arbitrary way by assigning it a different relation to concentration. For example, we regularly define the activity of a pure solvent as equal to 1; i. e., we identify the pure solvent as the standard state. The development here of the concepts of the *activity*, the *activity coefficient* and the dependency of μ on the concentration has been extensively simplified. A more complete treatment should include discussion of the laws of solutions (Raoult's law, Henry's law, etc.) and of the principal ways of expressing concentrations (mole fractions, molality, molarity). Consult a textbook of physical chemistry for fuller consideration.

103

✳ The activity of a solute is clearly then a quantity rather similar to its concentration. It may be regarded as the *effective concentration* of *A*, which can in fact be obtained from the *stoichiometric concentration* by use of a correction factor, the *activity coefficient*. The activity coefficient, γ (Greek letter *gamma*), is the quantity by which the concentration must be multiplied to obtain the activity, thus

$$a_A = \gamma [A]$$

Under the conditions stated, as the concentration approaches zero, the ☐activity ☐activity coefficient approaches a value of 1 as a limit.

104

✳ Of the two equations just introduced,

$$\mu_A = \mu_A^0 + RT \ln [A]$$

and $\qquad \mu_A = \mu_A^0 + RT \ln a_A$

the one that serves as a definition of the activity is the ☐first ☐second. The one based directly on experimental observation is the ☐first ☐second. (Indeed the experimental support for this equation is the only justification for the other one.) Which equation is inherently applicable at all concentrations? _____ .

102

activity

103

activity coefficient

104

second

first

the second
$(\mu_A = \mu_A^0 + RT\ ln\ a_A)$

105

✱ For biological systems the assumption is usually made that concentrations are low enough so that we are justified in using the approximate form of the equation, namely,

$$\mu_A = \underline{\hspace{3cm}}$$

Although the resulting errors may be significant, we often have little choice about the matter because we deal with compartments within the cell in which activities can scarcely be measured.

105

The full equation:
$\mu_A = \mu_A^0 + RT\ ln\ [A]$

106

✱ We are now in a position to construct the equation for the free energy change in a chemical reaction in terms of the concentrations of the participating substances. Recall that for the reaction

$$aA + bB \rightarrow eE + fF$$
$$\Delta G = (e\mu_E + f\mu_F) - (a\mu_A + b\mu_B)$$

Replace the quantities μ_A, μ_B, etc., in this equation with their equivalent values indicated by the equation,

$$\mu_A = \mu_A^0 + RT\ ln\ [A]$$

$$\Delta G = \underline{\hspace{4cm}}$$

107

✳ By collecting separately the terms containing μ^0 and the terms of the form $RT \, ln \, x$, we can reach the equation,

$$\varDelta G = \varDelta G^0 + RT \, ln \, \frac{[E]^e \times [F]^f}{[A]^a \times [B]^b}$$

The terms containing μ^0 have been represented here by the symbol _____ which is equal to

$$e\mu_E^0 + f\mu_F^0 - (a\mu_A^0 + b\mu_B^0)$$

108

✳ The expression obtained in the previous item, which can also be written, using the conversion factors at the back of the book, as follows,

$$\varDelta G = \varDelta G^0 + 2.303RT \, log \, \frac{[E]^e \times [F]^f}{[A]^a \times [B]^b}$$

is therefore the result we were looking for at the beginning of this section in Item 85. It defines the free energy change as a function of the concentrations of reactants and products in the reaction

$$aA + bB \rightarrow eE + fF$$

In this equation $[A]$ is the _____ of component A, etc., and $\varDelta G^0$, which is called the *standard free energy change*, is a quantity which ☐does ☐does not vary as the concentrations change, although its value does depend on the temperature and pressure at which the reaction occurs.

106

The full equation:

$$\varDelta G = e\mu_E^0 + eRT \, ln \, [E] + f\mu_F^0$$
$$+ fRTln[F] - (a\mu_A^0 + aRTln[A]$$
$$+ b\mu_B^0 + bRT \, ln \, [B])$$

107

$\varDelta G^0$

108

concentration

does not

The Standard Free Energy Change

109

✻ The equation of Item 108 shows us that when all the participating substances are at $1M$ concentration (or unit activity), the free energy change is equal to the _____

_____ .

109

standard free energy
change

110

✻ If we determine the free energy change for a known set of concentrations, we can use this equation to calculate the *standard free energy change*, which is the value recorded in tables and used for general comparisons.* Conversely, we can then use the equation to proceed from the standard free energy change to the free energy change applying for any given set of concentrations.

Do these statements mean that the experimental determination of ΔG^0 must be made at 1 M activity for each participating species? _____ .

---

*For biological systems the standard free energy change is often listed for pH 7, i.e., for $[H^+] = 10^{-7}$ M rather than 1 M, other components kept at unit activity. The symbol $\Delta G'$ is then used instead of ΔG^0. If H^+ is not a reactant, $\Delta G'$ and ΔG^0 should be the same.

111

✱ You may have noticed that the large algebraic fraction in the equation of Item 108 has the same form as that used under the mass action law to calculate the equilibrium constant* of a reaction:

$$\frac{[E]_{eq}^{e} \times [F]_{eq}^{f}}{[A]_{eq}^{a} \times [B]_{eq}^{b}} = K'_{eq}$$

Note, however, that the concentrations in the latter equation ☐may be any whatever ☐must be a set representing the state of equilibrium.   To emphasize this point, we have introduced the subscript *eq* for each concentration.

112

✱ Hence, by substitution, we may write *for the equilibrium condition,*

$$\Delta G_{eq} = \Delta G^{0} + RT \ln K'_{eq}$$

Recall once more that at equilibrium the value of ΔG is _____ . Solve the equation just stated, to yield a definition of the standard free energy change in terms of the equilibrium constant.

$$\Delta G^{0} = \underline{\hspace{3cm}}$$

*The prime mark is used when K_{eq} is stated in terms of *concentrations* rather than *activities* of the participating species.

110

No

111

must be a set representing the state of equilibrium

112

zero (Item 50)

The complete equation reads:

$$\Delta G^0 = - RT \ln K'_{eq}$$

113

✱ Suppose we mix ethyl alcohol and acetic acid, with the purpose of forming ethyl acetate (plus water). After 15 min at a selected temperature and pressure, we determine the proportions of the four substances. Suppose we were to calculate the standard free energy change for the reaction according to the equation of Item 112 from the value of

$$\frac{[\text{ethyl acetate}] \times [H_2O]}{[\text{acetic acid}] \times [\text{ethanol}]}$$

Neglecting the error arising from our using concentrations instead of activities, what have we failed to do correctly?

☐ 1. We should have ignored the concentration of water.

☐ 2. We should have checked that the concentrations were no longer changing with time, i.e., that equilibrium had been reached.

114

✳ The equation you just derived,

$$\Delta G^0 = - RT \ln K'_{eq},$$

can of course be rewritten

$$\Delta G^0 = - 2.303 \, RT \log K'_{eq}$$

The equilibrium constant has been determined for the reaction
glucose-1-phosphate $\rightarrow$ glucose-6-phosphate catalyzed by the enzyme, phosphoglucomutase, and a value of 17 was obtained at 25 °C. Calculate the standard free energy change for this reaction:

$$\Delta G^0 = \underline{\hspace{3cm}} \text{cal/mole}$$

(See inside back cover for the value of RT at 25 °C and for a table of logarithms.)

115

✳ By definition, this free energy change applies to the reaction when glucose-1-phosphate and glucose-6-phosphate are each 1 M in the same solution. Note that it does not tell us that the reaction will go rapidly in that case. In which direction will the reaction tend to proceed, given that an active phosphoglucomutase is present, toward formation of glucose-1-phosphate, or toward formation of glucose-6-phosphate? $\underline{\hspace{4cm}}$.

113

☐1. We should have ignored...
(Only for reactions occurring in dilute water solution do we regard the activity of water constant at unity.)

☑2. We should have checked that the concentrations were no longer changing with time...*

114

$\Delta G^0 = - (2.303)$
$(1.99) (298) (\log 17)$
$= - 1680$ cal/mole
$(- 7030$ joules/mole$)$

---

*The correctness of this response depends on our having otherwise observed that the reaction in question does proceed rapidly enough for us to observe changes in concentration within the time intervals selected. Reliable identification of the equilibrium position requires that we show that the same position is approached from either side—i.e., beginning with excesses of acetic acid and ethanol, and of ethyl acetate and water. When we purposely shift a system out of equilibrium so that we can observe the return toward equilibrium, we often say we *perturb* the system. This procedure is also important for kinetic studies.

115

glucose-6-phosphate
(The process proceeds
spontaneously in
the direction of
decreasing free
energy.)

116

$\log K'_{eq} = -1830/$
$(2.303 \times 1.99$
$\times 298) = -1.341$

$K'_{eq} = \dfrac{1}{21.9} = 0.0456$
dihydroxyacetone
phosphate, 21.9

116

✳ The standard free energy change for the reaction

dihydroxyacetone phosphate →
glyceraldehyde-3-phosphate

is +1.830 kcal/mole at 25 °C. Calculate the equilibrium constant.

$$K'_{eq} = \underline{\hspace{4cm}}.$$

From this constant, calculate which phosphate ester will be the more abundant at equilibrium, and by how many times, given that the presence of an enzyme permits equilibrium to be reached? _____ by _____ times.

117

The next five items discuss another important means of determining the standard free energy change of a reaction. The method of determining ΔG^0 just described is often excluded because the equilibrium lies so far to one side or the other that good analytical values cannot be obtained for all components. Would it be acceptable to set up several successive reactions leading from the reactants to the products, and then to summate algebraically the values for ΔG^0 obtained at the several steps? _____ .

Indeed, this procedure has been applied so extensively that the standard free energies of formation of many compounds *from their elements* are known and used in such calculations. The values for ΔG^0 for decomposing the reactants to their elements can then be added to the values of ΔG^0 for forming the products from the same elements, to obtain ΔG^0 for the reaction.

In such procedures, we must always specify the standard state to which ΔG^0 refers. For a substance in solution, we have already specified that the standard state is ☐an activity of 1 ☐the pure solute.

Yes (See Item 26.)

an activity of 1
(Item 102)

The conventional standard state for an element is also arbitrary; it generally is taken to be the pure element in its standard form at a given temperature and pressure, usually 25 °C and 1 atm. For the element oxygen, O_2 gas at 25 °C and 1 atm pressure is selected. For elementary carbon, graphite at 25 °C is used, and so on. Using these standard states we can obtain for various compounds the *standard free energy of formation*, ΔG_f^0, representing the free energy change when the contained elements in their respective standard states are united to form the compound in its standard state. For example,

$$H_2 \text{ (gas, 1 atm)} + 1/2 \ O_2 \text{ (gas, 1 atm)} \rightarrow$$
$$H_2O \text{ (pure liquid, 1 atm)}$$
$$\Delta G_f^0 = -56.69 \text{ kcal/mole at } 25 \text{ °C}$$

A student mixes oxygen and hydrogen gases, each at 1 atm, and notes no formation of water. This result appears inconsistent with the value just given for the standard free energy of water formation. Can one always tell whether a reaction is spontaneous or not from the promptness (or lack thereof) with which it occurs? _____ .

The standard free energies of formation of two substances can then be used to calculate by difference the standard free energy change for their interconversion. Consider, for example, the calculation of the free energy for the formation of glucose from CO_2 and H_2O:

$$6(CO_2 \rightarrow C + O_2)$$
$$\Delta G = - 6 \cdot \Delta G_f^0 = + 565.56 \text{ kcal}^\dagger \quad (1)$$

$$6(H_2O \rightarrow H_2 + 1/2 \ O_2)$$
$$\Delta G = - 6 \cdot \Delta G_f^0 = + 340.14 \text{ kcal} \quad (2)$$

Total free energy of decomposition of reactions (1) and (2):

$$\Delta G^0 = \underline{\hspace{3cm}} \text{ kcal}$$
$$6C + 6H_2 + 3O_2 \rightarrow C_6H_{12}O_6 \text{ (solid)} \quad (3)$$
$$\Delta G = \Delta G_f^0 = -217.56 \text{ kcal}$$

Net reaction, (1) + (2) + (3):

$$6CO_2 + 6H_2O \rightarrow C_6H_{12}O_6 + 6O_2$$
$$\Delta G^0 = \underline{\hspace{4cm}} \text{kcal/mole}$$

Note that we used the standard free energy of formation for solid glucose in this calculation. If the desired product was to be glucose in solution, we would use ☐ the same value ☐ a slightly different value for its ΔG_f^0.

No (Although the value of ΔG^0 predicts that they can react spontaneously, the reaction in this case is of course imperceptible. Item 131 of the Kinetics program will consider why reactions with large negative values of ΔG may fail to occur under ordinary conditions. A catalyst may be needed to show their spontaneity.*)

---

*We realize that reminders on this point are likely to prove tedious, but our experience shows that a significant number of students nevertheless need reinforcement on the matter.

†We must use the negative of the standard free energy of formation because we are considering the reversal of the formation reaction. As we noted earlier in a footnote to Item 66, this sign change on reversal of the process is characteristic of all thermodynamic functions that depend on the state of the system.

120

+ 905.70 kcal

+ 688.14 kcal

a slightly different
value

121

We have noted, then, that two principal methods are used for determining the standard free energy change for a chemical reaction.

Below are two equations, each of which serves for one of these methods. State in words the method corresponding to each equation

$$\Delta G^0 = \Delta G^0_f \text{ (products)} - \Delta G^0_f \text{ (reactants)}$$

ΔG^0 is obtained by _____

_____

_____

_____ .

$$\Delta G^0 = -2.303 \, RT \log \frac{[E]^e_{eq} \times [F]^f_{eq}}{[A]^a_{eq} \times [B]^b_{eq}}$$

ΔG^0 is obtained by _____

_____

_____

_____ .

✱ Consider from the equation

$$\varDelta G = \varDelta G^0 + 2.303 \; RT \log \frac{[E]^e \times [F]^f}{[A]^a \times [B]_b}$$

whether $\varDelta G$ and $\varDelta G^0$ will necessarily have the same sign._____.

Accordingly, does the sign of the standard free energy change (whether plus or minus) suffice to tell us in which direction a reaction will tend to proceed spontaneously in the living cell, given the presence of any needed enzymes?

_____.

summating the energies of formation of the products from their elements, and subtracting the total energies of formation of the reactants from their elements

measuring the concentrations of all reactants and products at equilibrium to obtain the value of K'_{eq}
(or equivalent words)

No

No (This information tells us only in which direction the reaction will tend to go at 1 M activities of all components. The real set of relative concentrations may cause this tendency to be reversed.)

Coupled Biological Reactions; "High-Energy Bonds"

123

✱ Knowledge of the free energy change of a given reaction is useful not only to predict whether the reaction will proceed spontaneously, but also to determine whether it can provide enough energy to drive a second, energy-requiring reaction. For example, the standard free energy change to form a peptide bond between the carboxyl group of leucine and the amino group of glycine in water solution is 3.5 kcal/mole at 25 °C. Calculate the final equilibrium concentration of leucylglycine that could theoretically be reached if leucine and glycine in the cell are each maintained at a steady-state concentration of 1 millimolar (mM). The activity of water can be taken as 1. (See inside of back cover for log table.)

$[\text{LeuGly}]_{eq} = $ _____.

Clearly, significant amounts of leucylglycine ☐can ☐cannot form spontaneously at physiological concentrations of the two amino acids.

✱ But in the living cell this reaction is coupled to the hydrolysis of *ATP* to *AMP* and pyrophosphate in such a way that part of the energy of that hydrolysis ($\Delta G'$ about -8 kcal/mole) can serve to drive formation of the peptide bond:

glycine + leucine + $ATP \rightarrow$
$$\text{leucylglycine} + P{-}P + AMP$$

The total reaction (even though it takes place in several steps) has a net $\Delta G'$ of -4.5 kcal/mole.

Thus, we see that *ATP* shows sufficient free energy of hydrolysis to drive the formation of the peptide bond under standard conditions.

Consider carefully, as a chemical problem: Does such a calculation mean that leucylglycine will tend to be formed if *ATP* is cleaved enzymatically to *AMP* and $P{-}P$ in a solution also containing leucine and glycine? _____.

$[\text{LeuGly}]_{eq}$
    $= 2.7 \times 10^{-9} M$
Method:

$3.5 = -1.364 \ \log \ \dfrac{[\text{LeuGly}]}{(10^{-3})^2}$

$\log [\text{LeuGly}] - \log 10^{-6} = -2.56$
$\log [\text{LeuGly}] = -8.56$
$\log [\text{LeuGly}] = 0.44 - 9$
$[\text{LeuGly}] = 2.7 \times 10^{-9} M$

(Give yourself special satisfaction if you got this one right.)

cannot

124

No (The two re-actions must, of course, be *coupled* —that is to say, have one or more common interme-diates. In this case, the acyl anhy-dride of leucine with AMP is form-ed, which then reacts spontane-ously with glycine in another enzy-matic step.)

125

✱ We may note, in passing, a defect in our ordi-nary biochemical terminology. We frequently refer to "the breakage of the high-energy bond" in the hydrolysis of *ATP*, whether to form *AMP* and pyrophosphate ion, or *ADP* and the orthop-hosphate ion, or in its reaction with leucine to form *AMP*-leucine anhydride and pyrophos-phate, during which

☐ 1. the bond joining a phosphoryl group to the rest of the *ATP* structure is simply burst asunder.

☐ 2. another structure (e.g., the *OH* group of water, or the acyl residue of leucine) merely takes the place of the structure to which a phosphorus atom was joined in *ATP*.

125

☐1. the bond...is simply burst...
(Literally, this ex-planation calls for the formation of highly reactive free radicals by pulling the *ATP* molecule apart.)

☑2. another structure... merely takes the place of...

126

✱ Therefore, the purist tends to prefer to speak of

☐ 1. energy released by the *breakage of a high-energy bond*.

☐ 2. the free energy change of *phosphoryl group transfer* from *ATP* to a new acceptor.

The next five items assume that you have studied the biochemical subjects discussed or are doing so simultaneously. If you have not, skip Item 132.

Here are listed a number of phosphorus compounds containing a so-called high-energy bond, along with others of the so-called low-energy type:

	$\Delta G'$ of hydrolysis, cal*
phosphoenolpyruvate	− 14,800
1, 3-diphosphoglycerate†	− 11,800
phosphocreatine	− 10,300
acetylphosphate	− 10,000
phosphoarginine	− 9,000
ATP†	− 7,300
glucose-1-phosphate	− 5,000
fructose-6-phosphate	− 3,800
glucose-6-phosphate	− 3,300
glycerol-1-phosphate	− 2,200

The standard free energy of hydrolysis of *ATP* to _____ and P_i, evaluated after a number of years of careful study, is ☐typical of the high-energy group ☐somewhat intermediate between the two classes.

☐1. energy released by breakage...

☑2. the free energy change of *phosphoryl group transfer*...

(The first terminology is, of course, a well established one, even if erroneous. Note also that the energy content is not correctly assigned to one particular bond but rather to the entire electronic distribution in that part of the molecule.)

---

*To convert to joules, multiply by 4.184.
†Hydrolysis of acyl phosphate bond.
†Formation of *ADP* and orthophosphate. A value of about − 8000 cal applies for formation of *AMP* and pyrophosphate.

127

128

ADP

somewhat interme-
diate

This position permits ATP to have a mediating role between the two classes of organic phosphorus compounds. It is somewhat beyond the scope of this program to account for the difference in the free energy of hydrolysis of these two classes. We may note, however, that in addition to the reaction by which the elements of water are added,

$$CH_2 = C - COO^- \\ \quad | \\ \quad O \\ \quad | \\ ^-O - P - O^- \\ \quad \| \\ \quad O$$

$+ H_2O$ $\longrightarrow$

$$CH_2 = C - COO^- \\ \quad | \\ \quad OH \\ \quad + \\ \quad OH \\ \quad | \\ ^-O - P - O^- \\ \quad \| \\ \quad O$$

phospho*enol*pyruvate

another reaction follows

$$CH_2 = C - COO^- \\ \quad | \\ \quad OH$$

$\longrightarrow$

$$CH_3 - C - COO^- \\ \qquad \| \\ \qquad O$$

*enol*pyruvate

*keto*pyruvate

and that the value of $\Delta G' = -14{,}800$ cal covers both reactions.

For the latter reaction, we will take K'_{eq},

$$\left[\begin{matrix} CH_3 - C - COO^- \\ \| \\ O \end{matrix} \right] \Big/ \left[\begin{matrix} CH_2 = C - COO^- \\ | \\ OH \end{matrix} \right],$$ to equal

about 10^8 at pH 7. From this value we can calculate that $\Delta G' = $ _____ cal.

Of the total free energy change on hydrolysis of phospho*enol*pyruvate to *keto*pyruvate and P_i we can therefore attribute about _____ cal to the hydrolytic stage *per se,* the first reaction shown above.

129

For the other high-energy compounds listed, a H^+ spontaneously adds to or dissociates from the product of the simple addition of the elements of water to contribute a portion of the total ☐decrease ☐increase in free energy.

The hydrolysis of glycerol phosphate and of the sugar phosphates listed ☐is ☐is not followed by a second reaction, the free energy change of which must be added.

130

In two of the high-energy compounds in our list, the phosphorus is bonded directly to a N atom, namely in _____ and

_____.

$$O=\overset{\displaystyle O^-}{\underset{\displaystyle O^-}{P}}\sim \overset{\displaystyle H}{N}-\overset{\displaystyle \overset{+}{N}H_2}{C}-\overset{\displaystyle CH_3}{N}-CH_2C\overset{\displaystyle O^-}{\underset{\displaystyle O}{\diagdown}}$$

In this formula for phosphocreatine, the so-called high-energy bond is represented by the symbol $\sim$, called a *squiggle*. Go back to Item 128 and introduce a squiggle into phospho*enol*-pyruvate.

Will the purist be pleased with the convention of the squiggle (Item 126)? _____.

128

about $-10,900$
$(-1,364 \times 8)$

-3900

129

decrease

is not

130

phosphocreatine, phosphoarginine (Either order. The first of these is a characteristic reservoir of bond energy in vertebrates, whereas the second is found in many invertebrates.)

$$CH_2 = C - COO^-$$
$$|$$
$$O$$
$$\wr$$
$$^-O - P - O^-$$
$$\|$$
$$O$$

(Don't be disconcerted if you placed the squiggle one position higher, between C and O.
Experiments with ^{18}O have shown that it is the P—O, not the C—O bond, at which cleavage occurs.)

No

131

The transfer of the phosphoryl group

$$O^-$$
$$|$$
$$-P = O$$
$$|$$
$$O^-$$

from one of the compounds to form another of the compounds listed in Item 127 or among other phosphoric acid derivatives, without an energy wasting release of P_i and an organic product, depends on the presence of an appropriate phosphoryl group-transferring enzyme called a *phosphokinase* or *phosphotransferase*.

From the values of the standard free energy of hydrolysis, we may judge that, given the presence of the proper ☐phosphagen ☐phosphokinase, phosphocreatine can be formed from ATP plus creatine

☐ 1. under no circumstances whatever.

☐ 2. only if the concentrations of ATP and creatine are sufficiently higher than those of ADP and phosphocreatine.

131

phosphokinase

☑2. only if the con-
centrations...
(ΔG can become negative under these
conditions, even
though the $\Delta G'$
for formation is
strongly positive.)

OXIDATION-REDUCTION REACTIONS: ELECTROCHEMICAL CELLS AND OXIDATION-REDUCTION POTENTIALS

Electrochemical Work; The Nernst Equation

132

✱ We have seen that one chemical reaction can drive another if the first releases more energy than is required to drive the second, and if they are appropriately _____ with each other.

coupled (linked)

✱ We will now discuss a type of coupling in which *the electron* produced by one chemical process is utilized by another. The total of these two events is called an *oxidation-reduction* reaction. Our objective in this section will be to develop another means of determining the free energy change in such reactions, that is, through determination of the *oxidation-reduction potentials* of the reactants. We will see that this determination also provides us with a relatively simple means of discussing processes of biological electron transport and a way for measuring pH.

An oxidation-reduction reaction can often be made to do electrical work by causing it to take place in an electrical cell. This is an arrangement by which the electron flow from one part of the reaction to the other is made to occur through an electrical conductor. Conversely, we can do work on the system by forcing current to flow through the cell with an external voltage source.

As we have come to expect, thermodynamics concerns itself with ☐the rate at which such a reaction can proceed ☐the maximal work the reaction can be made to do, or the minimal work required to drive the reaction.

✱ We are able to measure the minimal work required to drive a reaction of this type in an especially direct way. The work required to drive the reaction depends on the tendency of one part of the reaction to release electrons in relation to the tendency of the other part to accept electrons; that is, it depends on the net voltage produced by the cell.

The minimum work in calories required to drive n gram-equivalents of electrons against a voltage, V, is given by

$$W = - nFV$$

where F is the Faraday constant, equal to 23,061 cal/volt-equivalent. Thus, to drive 1 gram-equivalent of electrons against –0.2 volt requires an amount of work ☐smaller than ☐equal to ☐greater than the amount of work required to drive 2 gram-equivalents of electrons against -0.1 volt, namely _____ cal.

the maximal work..., or the minimal work...

134

equal to

4612 cal

135

✱ To be able to calculate the *minimal work* required to drive a chemical reaction, we need only to measure the voltage produced by the electrical cell against which we must drive electrons in order to cause the reaction to take place.

(Note that this is also the maximal voltage produced by the reverse reaction, which can do work.)

As this equation shows,

$$\Delta G = W'_{min} = - nFV_{reaction}$$

the value of the minimal work will tell us the change in _____ characteristic of the reaction.

135

free energy

136

✱ This voltage is called the *electrical potential* (or the *electromotive force*) of the reaction. It is designated by the symbol E.

Make the substitution proposed by the preceding sentence in the equation just given.

$$\Delta G = - \text{_____}$$

137

* The figure below shows a very simple electrical cell, one that uses the reaction,

$$CuSO_4 + Zn \rightarrow Cu + ZnSO_4$$

We can write this reaction more strictly by omitting the sulfate ions, which do not participate:

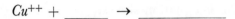

$$Cu^{++} + _____ \rightarrow __________$$

(The reader may recall from former experience that this reaction proceeds spontaneously in the direction in which it is written here.)

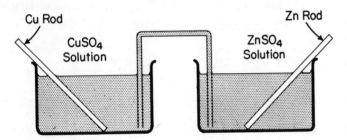

Cu Rod
Zn Rod
CuSO4 Solution
ZnSO4 Solution

(Do not be concerned that no metallic conductor has yet been provided between the electrodes.)

136

The full equation:
$\Delta G = -nFE$

137

The full equation:
$$Cu^{++} + Zn \rightarrow$$
$$Cu + Zn^{++}$$
(the products in either order, of course)

138

∗ Note that the cell is constructed with a "salt bridge," a glass tube filled with agar gel containing an electrolyte, perhaps KCl. If we did not interpose some such porous barrier between the two solutions, but instead placed them in immediate contact, they would mix, and the attack of Cu^{++} on the Zn electrode would occur spontaneously and uncontrollably.∗ This result would be thermodynamically unsatisfactory to our purpose of measuring the maximal work the cell can do, because (check all statements that are pertinent explanations)

☐ 1. we should then expect much of the energy to be released as heat.

☐ 2. a process must be controlled by making it do maximal work, i.e., by causing it to occur in a reversible fashion, if we are to measure the free energy change characteristic of it.

☐ 3. one would not be able to observe the maximal voltage against which the flow of electrons from the zinc electrode to the copper electrode can occur.

---

*If you wonder why we need any bridge at all, consider that the removal of Cu^{++} to form copper metal would leave a deficiency of cations in one vessel; the formation of zinc ion from zinc metal would create a cation excess in the other. For the cell to operate continuously and to generate a current, ions must be able to pass through the bridge to relieve these disparities.

✳ Since zinc metal tends to become Zn^{++} and Cu^{++} tends to become copper metal, we will note that one of the electrodes tends to become depleted, the other enriched with electrons, relatively speaking. The quantities of electrons involved are immeasurably small, but nevertheless they cause the two electrodes to become charged, with reference to each other. Consider carefully whether each of these spontaneous processes tends to yield electrons to the rod, or to remove them from it. Mark on the sketch which electrode tends to become positive, and which negative.

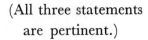

(All three statements are pertinent.)

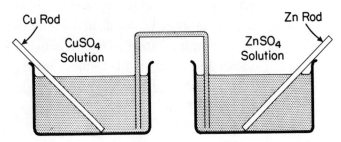

Cu Rod   Zn Rod

CuSO₄ Solution   ZnSO₄ Solution

139

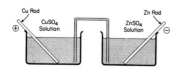

(Note that the copper electrode will tend to become deficient in electrons [i.e., positive] as Cu^{++} takes up electrons and is converted to copper metal.)

140

No

140

✳ Each of the electrode vessels in our sketch can be called a *half-cell*, since it takes both to constitute a complete electrical cell. The two reactions, one occurring in each of the half-cells,

$$Cu^{++} + 2e^- \rightleftharpoons Cu$$
$$Zn \rightleftharpoons Zn^{++} + 2e^-$$

are called *half-cell reactions*. It is these paired reactions that are *coupled* because one of them uses the electrons released by the other.

Under the arrangement sketched, will either half-cell reaction proceed to completion? That is, will the zinc rod dissolve in the zinc sulfate solution, and the cupric ion plate out on the copper electrode? _____.

141

✳ It is important to note, however, that each half-cell reaction *proceeds constantly in both directions,* as indicated above by the double arrows. Furthermore, each reaction shows infinitesimal *net progress* to the right as written, and will, as inspection of the equations shows, infinitesimally impoverish the ☐copper ☐zinc electrode in electrons and enrich the _____ electrode with electrons, one with reference to the other. We can discover that this has happened by attaching a conductor between the rods and noting an electron flow from the ☐copper ☐zinc to the _____ electrode.

142

✱ The total reaction can proceed, a half-cell reaction in each compartment, when this electron flow is permitted.

To measure the maximal tendency of this current to flow we should

☐ 1. oppose it with a known voltage just sufficient to stop the flow.

☐ 2. permit 1 gram-equivalent of *Cu* to be plated out on the copper electrode and see how much current passed through the conductor in the meantime.

143

✱ Under these conditions, any tiny amount of electron flow that occurs would represent
☐ a reversible   ☐ an irreversible   process.

141

copper, zinc

zinc, copper

142

☑ 1. oppose it with a known...
(The other test serves a quite different, although interesting, purpose—i.e., to determine the value of the Faraday constant.)

143

a reversible

144

* By that procedure we find that when both $CuSO_4$ and $ZnSO_4$ are at 1 M concentrations at 25°, an electromotive force of 1.100 volts can be observed between the two electrodes. We can therefore take the equation,

$$\Delta G = -nFE,$$

and introduce the following values:

n = 2 gram-equivalents of electrons per mole (note that we generally calculate the free energy change *per mole*)

F = 23,061 cal per volt-equivalent

E = 1.100 volts

ΔG = ______________ cal/mole

144

$$\Delta G = (-2)(23{,}061)(1.1) = -50{,}730 \text{ cal/mole}$$

145

* We have seen that the free energy change of a reaction depends on the concentration of the reactants and the products, according to the equation

$$\Delta G = \Delta G^0 + 2.303\ RT\ log \frac{[D]^d \times [E]^e}{[A]^a \times [B]^b}$$

Will the electromotive force of our electric cell change with the concentrations of the $CuSO_4$ and the $ZnSO_4$? __________. Which must we increase to increase the EMF? __________. (You can tell by recalling that the two equations of Item 140 tend to proceed to the right.)

INTRODUCTION TO BIOENERGETICS: THERMODYNAMICS FOR THE BIOLOGIST

146

✱ We will define a *standard electrode potential, E^0,* for any given oxidation-reduction reaction as follows:

$$E^0 = -\Delta G^0/nF$$

Since $\Delta G^0 = -2.303\ RT \log K'_{eq}$ (Item 112), we can write $E^0 = \dfrac{2.303\ RT}{(\underline{\qquad})} \log K'_{eq}$

(Supply the denominator for this fraction.)

147

✱ Furthermore, by substituting nFE and nFE^0 for ΔG and ΔG^0 in the equation in Item 145, we can write,

$$E = E^0 - \frac{2.303\ RT}{nF} \log \frac{[D]^d \times [E]^e}{[A]^a \times [B]^b}$$

Obtain the value of the quantity $2.303\ RT/F$ in volt-equivalents at 25 °C, using the table at the back of the book if necessary: _____ volt-equivalents. Simplify the equation accordingly.

$$E = \underline{\hspace{6cm}}$$

145

Yes

CuSO₄

146

The complete equation:

$$E^0 = \frac{2.303\ RT}{nF} \log K_{eq}$$

147

0.0592 volt-
equivalent.
The complete
equation:

$$E = E^0 - \frac{0.0592}{n}$$

$$\times \log \frac{[D]^d \times [E]^e}{[A]^a \times [B]^b}$$

148

✱ This important equation is known as the *Nernst equation*. It provides us with one more means of determining the standard free energy change of a reaction, if we can devise a means for measuring what EMF the reaction will generate under a known set of conditions. Note that we used standard conditions (pure metallic electrodes; 1 M $CuSO_4$ and $ZnSO_4$) in determining the voltage of the simple cell we have been discussing. Therefore, what is the numerical value of the *standard electrode potential* for that reaction? _____ . The standard free energy change? _____ .

148

1.100 volts

$- 50,730$ cal/mole

149

✱ Suppose for the same electrical cell we were to dilute the copper sulfate to 0.5 M without changing the $ZnSO_4$ concentration in the other half-cell. Calculate the new electromotive force to four significant figures.

$$E = \underline{\hspace{2cm}} \text{ volts}$$

✻ Oxidation-reduction reactions are the only type of chemical reactions that can generate an electromotive force; hence, such measurements can be made for them only. Even then it may not be possible to design electrodes that can receive the electrons released by one component and pass them to the other component. In our example both electrodes took direct part in the reaction: zinc ion was released into solution from the zinc electrode; copper metal was deposited on the copper electrode. Frequently, however, the electrode is not a primary reactant. Sometimes it can nevertheless be caused to take part in a catalytic way. Consider the half-cell reaction:

$$H_2 \rightleftharpoons 2H^+ + 2e^-$$

Platinum electrodes can be especially designed so that they accelerate the attainment of equilibrium for this reaction. As a result, such a platinum electrode, when kept saturated with hydrogen gas and in contact with a solution containing H^+, is able to donate or receive the electrons participating in this half-cell reaction.

Consider an entirely different example: The enzymatic interconversion of amino acids and keto acids (transamination) might be represented as follows:

$$RCH(NH_3^+)COO^- + OH^- \rightleftharpoons R\overset{O}{\overset{\|}{C}}-COO^- + 2e^- + NH_4^+ + H^+$$

Obviously this ☐is ☐is not an oxidation-reduction reaction. Does that mean we can determine ΔG for the reaction by directly measuring the electromotive force contributed by it? _____ .

$$= 1.100$$
$$- \frac{0.059}{2} \log \frac{1}{0.5}$$
$$= 1.100$$
$$- \frac{0.059 \times 0.30}{2}$$
$$= 1.100 - 0.0089$$
$$= 1.091 \text{ volts}$$

150

is

No
(Not unless electrode
systems can be
designed capable
of donating and
receiving, directly
or indirectly, the
electrons involved.)

151

can still, however

151

✱ We may not always be able to design electrodes
suitable for measuring the EMF of an oxidation-reduction reaction. Nor are we always
able to secure a coupling so that the electrons
released by one reaction can drive another.

If we can discover the electrical potential of
such a reaction, we ☐ can still, however
☐ cannot calculate the free-energy change
applicable to the reaction.

Standard Electrode Potentials

152

✱ Let us return to the subject of the so-called
half-cell reaction. Write such a reaction involving copper. _____

Can we cause such a reaction to proceed
to any substantial extent in isolation? _____ .

✱ Similarly, we cannot measure the tendency of this reaction to release or accept electrons except by hooking it to a source of electrons or to an electron sink —*e.g.,* another half-cell reaction—and measuring the potential against which the flow of electrons will occur.

We are therefore forced to state the half-cell potentials in relation to some arbitrary standard, much as we measure the heights of mountain peaks and the depth of the sea from an arbitrary standard, the sea level.

The platinum-hydrogen electrode just described is our generally accepted standard. Using the term $E^0_{\frac{1}{2}}$ for the standard electrode potential identified with a given half-cell whose components are in their standard state, we write arbitrarily that when $[H^+] = 1\ M$ and the pressure of H_2 is 1 atm, the value of _____ (supply the symbol) equals zero for the platinum-hydrogen electrode.

$$Cu^{++} + 2e^- \rightleftharpoons Cu$$

(either order; other possibilities exist, of course)

No

153

$E^0_{\frac{1}{2}}$

154

✻ Table I (see *Appendix B*) lists the standard electrode potentials for many reactions, including the two half-cell reactions we have been considering.

$$Zn^{++} + 2e^- \rightleftharpoons Zn \qquad E^0_{\frac{1}{2}} = -0.763 \text{ volt}$$
$$Cu^{++} + 2e^- \rightleftharpoons Cu \qquad E^0_{\frac{1}{2}} = +0.337 \text{ volt}$$

The tabulated values actually refer to the electromotive forces generated by the following reactions:

$$Zn^{++}(1\ M) + H_2(1\text{ atm}) \rightarrow$$
$$Zn(\text{solid}) + 2H^+(1\ M);\ E^0 = -0.763 \text{ volt}$$
$$Cu^{++}(1\ M) + H_2(1\text{ atm}) \rightarrow$$
$$Cu(\text{solid}) + 2H^+(1\ M);\ E^0 = +0.337 \text{ volt}$$

Since the potential of the platinum-hydrogen electrode is taken to be _____ , the total EMF is arbitrarily attributed to the other electrode.

The difference in the signs of E^0 here obviously has to do with the difference in the direction in which each of the reactions tends to go. The convention about signs will be discussed below.

In order to obtain the equation for the total reaction under consideration,

$$Cu^{++}(1\ M) + Zn(\text{solid}) \rightarrow$$
$$Cu(\text{solid}) + Zn^{++}(1\ M)$$

we must subtract the ☐first ☐second reaction above from the _____ one. If we apply the corresponding operation to the values of $E^0_{\frac{1}{2}}$, we obtain

$$E^0 = (0.337 \underline{\hspace{2cm}}) = +1.100 \text{ volts}$$

155

✳ Notice that this procedure is much the same as one of the methods we used in the preceding section for calculating free energy changes of reactions. In that case we arbitrarily chose for our standard state the *pure elements*. On that basis we tabulated free energies of formation of various compounds. If such calculations yield one value for the free energy of formation of glucose-1-phosphate, and another value for glucose-6-phosphate, we know that the difference between these two values will be the free energy change of the conversion of one of these esters into the other,

☐ 1. provided a reversible pathway is followed.

☐ 2. for any pathway whatever.

156

✳ Similarly, we should get the same result for the electromotive force for the cell

$$Cu \,|\, Cu^{++} \,|\,|\, Zn^{++} \,|\, Zn*$$

whether we measure it directly or obtain the value by an algebraic summation of the EMF values of two or more electrical cells in which these half-cells are included, provided that our algebraic summation is carried out in such a way as to correspond to the reaction

$$Cu^{++} + \underline{\hspace{3cm}}$$

154

zero

first, second

$-\,(-\,0.763)$ or
$+\,0.763$

155

☑ 2. for any pathway...
(The change in free energy is independent of the pathway.)

*Note the shorthand notation whereby the position of the salt bridge is represented by two vertical lines.

$+ Zn \rightarrow Cu + Zn^{++}$

✱ So far we have not dwelt on the problem: given the sign of the standard electrode potential, how do we recognize which electrode tends to be positive, which negative? We need to make that assignment to recognize from the sign on E^0 in which direction the reaction will tend to go spontaneously. The answer to this question depends on an arbitrary decision as to which end of an ordered sequence of half-cell reactions is regarded as most positive, which the most negative. That is, should we give the highest positive value to the strongest oxidant or the strongest reductant?

Fortunately a consistent convention in favor of the first of these two alternatives is now followed for reactions of biochemical interest.

First, one selects the electrode at which *reduction* (i.e., electron donation to the solution) occurs when the reaction proceeds as written.

For the reaction, $Cu^{++} + Zn \rightarrow Cu + Zn^{++}$, we would choose the ☐copper ☐zinc electrode.

✱ The electrical potential we observe at that electrode is taken to be the EMF of the reaction, both as to sign and magnitude, the potential of the other electrode being taken as zero.

The assignment for the reaction,

$$Zn^{++}(1\ M) + H_2(1\ atm) \rightarrow$$
$$Zn(\text{solid}) + 2H^+(1\ M)$$

of a value of -0.763 volt for the standard electrode potential (which we will now call the *standard electrode reduction potential* to emphasize the convention followed) means that an electromotive force of -0.763 volt was observed at the ☐zinc ☐platinum-H_2 electrode, with respect to the other electrode.

copper (Cu^{++} is reduced to Cu.)

✱ Note that when E^0 is positive, ΔG^0 is negative, since $\Delta G^0 = -nFE^0$. Therefore the negative sign on the value of E^0 for the $Zn - H_2$ cell means that ΔG^0 has a ☐negative ☐positive value, and hence that the reaction as written ☐is ☐is not spontaneous. That is, the overall reaction will tend spontaneously to ☐deposit zinc on the zinc electrode ☐dissolve the zinc electrode.

zinc

positive

is not

dissolve the zinc
electrode

✳ The statement that a value of $+0.337$ volt has been assigned for the standard _____

_____

(use specifically detailed terminology) for the half-cell Cu^{++}/Cu means that for the reaction

$$Cu^{++}(1\ M) + H_2(1\ atm) \rightarrow$$
$$Cu(\text{solid}) + 2H^+(1\ M)$$

an electromotive force of $+\ 0.337$ volt was observed at the ☐copper ☐platinum-H_2 electrode, relative to the _____ electrode. The overall reaction therefore tends in that case to ☐deposit copper on the copper electrode ☐dissolve the copper electrode.

---

electrode reduction
potential

copper

platinum-hydrogen

deposit copper...

✳ Our convention means that tables of standard electrode _____ potentials refer to reactions written in the following form:

$$A_{oxidized} + H_2 \rightarrow A_{reduced} + 2H^+$$

Then if $E_{\frac{1}{2}}^0$ is positive, ΔG^0 is _____, and the reaction proceeds spontaneously ☐as written ☐in the reverse of the direction written.

162

✳ This convention means that the more positive the electrode reduction potential, the greater the tendency of $A_{oxidized}$ to become reduced, and hence the ☐stronger ☐weaker an oxidizing agent (one that will *accept* electrons) it is.

163

✳ If we are told that a certain substance, $A_{reduced}$, is a powerful reducing agent, we shall expect a ☐high ☐low, perhaps highly negative, reduction potential to be assigned to the system,

$$A_{oxidized} + H_2 \rightarrow A_{reduced} + 2H^+$$

164

✳ If the concentrations of $A_{oxidized}$ and/or $A_{reduced}$ deviate from 1 M, the potential of the half-cell will no longer equal the standard electrode reduction potential. In that case we can write, from the Nernst equation for the reaction,

$$A_{oxidized} + \frac{n}{2} H_2(1 \text{ atm}) \rightarrow A_{reduced} + nH^+(1 \text{ } M)$$

that the potential for the half-cell

$$A_{oxidized} + ne^- \rightarrow A_{reduced}$$

$$E_{\frac{1}{2}} = E_{\frac{1}{2}}^0 - \frac{0.059}{n} \log \underline{\hspace{3cm}}$$

161

reduction

negative (or < 0)

☑as written

162

stronger

163

low, perhaps highly negative (A negative E means that the reaction will tend to go in the reverse direction.)

164

The complete equation:

$$E_{\frac{1}{2}} = E^0_{\frac{1}{2}} - \frac{0.059}{n} \log \frac{[A_{red}]}{[A_{ox}]}$$

(which can also be written

$$E_{\frac{1}{2}} = E^0_{\frac{1}{2}} + \frac{0.059}{n} \log \frac{[A_{ox}]}{[A_{red}]}).$$

(If you included $[H^+]$ and $[H_2]$ in your equation, note that these equalled $1M$ and 1 atm respectively, and cancel out.)

165

* Examine the list of oxidation-reduction couples of special biological interest in Table II (see *Appendix B*). Note first of all that in this table the standard electrode reduction potentials are designated $E'_{\frac{1}{2}}$ rather than $E^0_{\frac{1}{2}}$. This symbol $E'_{\frac{1}{2}}$ means that the standard potentials are for 10^{-7} M H^+ (i.e., pH 7) rather than for 1 M H^+, all other standard concentrations being unmodified.*

Check by use of the Nernst equation: is the value of -0.42 volt listed for the H^+/H_2 couple at pH 7.0 consistent with our decision to assign a value of 0.000 volt for E^0 for the platinum-hydrogen electrode? _____.

165

Yes (You can confirm with the Nernst equation that the EMF will be lowered by 0.42 volt by changing $[H^+]$ from 1 M to $10^{-7} M$: $E' = 0.000 + 0.059 \times \log 10^{-7}$).

*Just as we often use $\Delta G'$ for biochemical reactions, setting the standard $[H]$ at 10^{-7} M rather than 1 M, we also often use E' instead of E^0 for biological oxidation-reduction reactions.

Biological Examples

166

✳ From Table II in Appendix B it can be seen that ferredoxin, an important iron-containing protein in electron transport systems of photosynthesis and nitrogen fixation, (check one)

☐ 1. is a strong biological reductant (electron donor) when the iron is in the Fe^{2+} state.

☐ 2. is a strong biological oxidant (electron acceptor) when the iron is in the Fe^{3+} state.

167

✳ Determine from this table whether coenzyme Q under standard conditions is thermodynamically capable of reducing cytochrome c. _____ . Does that conclusion tell you whether oxidized cytochrome c will rapidly oxidize coenzyme Q when the two are mixed in solution? _____ .

166

☑1. is a strong biological reductant...

167

Yes

No (We encounter here the usual limitation of thermodynamic predictions. The electrons made available when coenzyme Q is oxidized may not be accepted by cytochrome c unless a suitable catalyst or mediator is present. The actual direction of the reaction will also depend on the relative concentrations or activities of the components.)

168

* By reference to Table **II** in Appendix B, calculate the standard free energy change at pH 7 for *complete* oxidation of $NADH$ according to the equation

$$NADH + H^+ + 1/2\ O_2 \rightarrow NAD^+ + H_2O$$

$$\Delta G' = \underline{\hspace{4cm}}$$

✱ We observed earlier that phosphorus compounds of the high-energy type can be formed directly during metabolism, for example in glycolysis (Items 127 to 131),

$$CH_2OH—CH—COO^-$$
$$\overset{|}{O}PO_3^=$$

$$\xrightarrow{—H_2O}$$

A simple ester

$$CH_2{=}C—COO^-$$
$$\overset{|}{O}PO_3^=$$

A phosphorylated enol

A much larger source of high-energy phosphoryl compounds is *oxidative phosphorylation.* The removal of H from substrates by catabolism leads very often to the reduction of NAD^+ to $NADH$. The following overall reaction shows how energy is conserved (i.e., stored) on the subsequent oxidation of $NADH$:

$$NADH + H^+ + 3ADP + 3\,P_i + 1/2\,O_2 \rightarrow$$
$$NAD^+ + 4H_2O + 3ATP$$

This reaction may be analyzed into an *exergonic* (energy-releasing) component,

$$NADH + H^+ + 1/2\,O_2 \rightarrow NAD^+ + H_2O$$
$$\Delta G' = -52,400 \text{ cal/mole } NADH$$

and an *endergonic* (energy-requiring) component,

$$3ADP + 3\,P_i \rightarrow 3ATP + 3H_2O$$
$$\Delta G' = +21,900 \text{ cal/3 moles } ATP$$

The free energy change for our overall reaction is _____ cal/mole $NADH$.

Under standard conditions the overall reaction ☐can ☐cannot proceed spontaneously.

$E' = 0.815$
$- (-0.320) =$
$+ 1.14$ volts

$\Delta G = -nFE' =$
$(-2)\,(23,061)$
$(1.14) = -52,350$
cal/mole
$(-219,000 \text{ joules/}$
mole)

169

— 30,500

can

170

✱ What per cent of the energy released by the exergonic component is conserved by the endergonic component?

Hence, we may say that the efficiency of coupling is _____ per cent.

Does the overall reaction as written above reveal any coupling between the two component reactions? _____.

✶ Accordingly, the above overall equation must fail to show all intermediates in the process of oxidative phosphorylation. Clearly, two electrons must be released when $NADH$ is converted to NAD^+. These electrons are known to be passed subsequently from one acceptor to another in the electron-transport chain, as shown in the accompanying figure, with oxygen serving as the final electron acceptor.

When we examine in Item 169 the endergonic component of our overall reaction, we see that the electron ☐is also ☐is not, however,   a reactant.

Does the figure below explicitly identify a step coupling electron transport to the generation of $ATP?$ _____.

41.8 (21,900/52,400)

41.8

No (No intermediate which contains important components of both reactions is shown.)

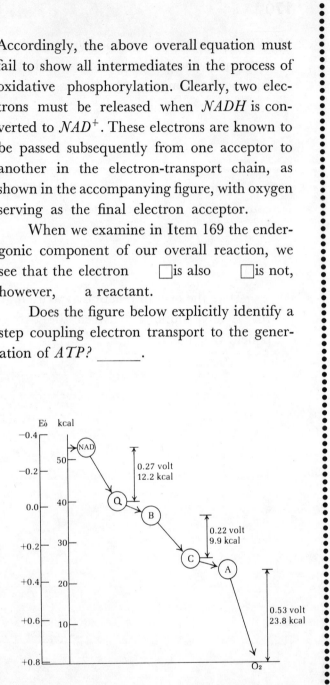

Diagram showing the energy relations of the electron-transport chain components. Electrons are passed from $NADH$ through flavoproteins to coenzyme Q(Q), cytochromes b(B), c(C), a(A) (in that order), and finally to oxygen.

(Reproduced, with permission, from Lehninger, A. L.: *Biochemistry*, Worth Publishers, Inc., New York, 1970)

171

is not, however,

No

172

✳ The nature of the coupling reactions and the coupling agents that permit electron transport to drive the formation of ATP from _____ and P_i in the intact mitochondrion is in a complicated stage of investigation. In Item 127 we considered the minimal amount of energy required to drive this reaction to be 7300 cal.

Examine the figure in Item 171 and suggest steps in electron transport that provide enough energy to permit generation of a high-energy phosphate bond:

☑ 1. $NADH$ to coenzyme Q
☐ 2. Coenzyme Q to cytochrome b
☑ 3. Cytochrome b to cytochrome c
☐ 4. Cytochrome c to cytochrome a
☑ 5. Cytochrome a to oxygen

The division of electron transport into several smaller stages, as pictured in the diagram (Item 171), is a biological solution to the problem of how to match efficiently the exergonic process of $NADH$ oxidation to endergonic reactions, to conserve energy.

173

It is only by historical accident that we use E^0 to measure the tendency of oxidation-reduction reactions to occur spontaneously, whereas for all other reactions we usually prefer to use ΔG^0. Still another form of expressing the tendency of reactions to occur spontaneously will be introduced in a companion program, *pH and Dissociation;* this is the pK' (the $-\log K'_{eq}$) for the dissociation of weak acids.

Note that if comparisons are to be made, we should choose to convert all such measures (ΔG^0, E^0, K'_{eq}, pK') to ΔG^0, rather than to calculate the values of E^0 for reactions that do not involve oxidation-reduction or values of $-\log K'_{eq}$ for all reactions.

This statement means that the unit in which the maximal work required to produce a given reaction is most suitably expressed is ☐calories (or joules) per mole ☐moles per liter ☐volts.

172

ADP

☑1. *NADH* to coenzyme Q

☐2. Coenzyme Q to cytochrome b

☑3. Cytochrome b to cytochrome c

☐4. Cytochrome c to cytochrome a

☑5. Cytochrome a to oxygen

173

calories (or joules)

per mole

Note To The Learner:

The remaining items in this section and all of the final section of this program deal with additional applications of the principles we have developed, including:

Measurement of pH: Concentration cells (Items 174–179)

An expanded definition of the chemical potential (Items 180–185)

Osmotic phenomena (Items 186–211)

Potential differences across membranes (Items 212–235)

Active transport (Items 236–263)

The Steady State: Nonequilibrium Thermodynamics (Items 246–265)

Study of these items should assist the student in gaining a better working knowledge of the thermodynamic concepts as well as a better understanding of these phenomena for their own sake. Should these goals not be important to the student, however, this study can of course be considered complete at this point, and he can proceed to summary Items 264-291. However, we deplore that omission.

Measurement of pH: Concentration Cells

174

As another example of the usefulness of measurements of electrode potentials, consider a cell that combines a platinum-hydrogen electrode with a calomel electrode (calomel is Hg_2Cl_2).

The half-cell reactions are as follows:

$$2H^+ + 2e^- \rightarrow H_2 \; (E^0_{\frac{1}{2}} = 0.000, \text{ by convention})$$

$$Hg_2Cl_2 \text{ (solid)} + 2e^- \rightarrow$$
$$2Hg \text{ (liquid)} + 2Cl^- \text{ (1 M)} \; (E^0_{\frac{1}{2}} = 0.280 \text{ volt})$$

The two electrode vessels are connected by a salt bridge. If we maintain the pressure of the hydrogen gas at 1 atm, but vary the hydrogen ion concentration for the reaction*

$$2Cl^- \text{ (1 M)} + 2Hg + 2H^+ \rightarrow$$
$$H_2 \text{ (1 atm)} + Hg_2Cl_2$$

we can set up the appropriate form of the Nernst equation as follows:

$$E = -0.280 - \frac{0.059}{2} \log \frac{[Hg_2Cl_2]\,[H_2]}{[H^+]^2\,[Hg]^2\,[Cl^-]^2}$$

According to the convention established in Items 157 to 158, this equation will give the potential of the ☐calomel ☐hydrogen electrode, with the _____ electrode as reference.

*The student should not be concerned to note that the reaction, as written, is not spontaneous in the direction indicated. Recall that it will go spontaneously in the opposite direction and that by opposing the electromotive force of the cell (i.e., by doing work on it), it is possible to drive the reaction in the indicated direction. In fact, cell potentials are usually measured by applying a voltage which is equal and opposite to the cell whose potential is to be measured.

Since four of the five components of this reaction are in their standard state,

$$[Hg] = [Cl^-] = [Hg_2Cl_2] = [H_2] = 1$$

we can simplify the equation thus

$$E = -0.280 - \frac{0.059}{2} \log \{1/[H^+]^2\}$$

$$E = -0.280 + 0.059 \log [H^+]$$

Note the following definition of the pH:

$$pH = -\log [H^+]$$

Convert our equation for the potential of the cell into a similar one in which one term is the pH of the solution.

$$E = \underline{\hspace{5cm}}$$

hydrogen

calomel (because, as the equation for the reaction is written, H^+ is reduced to H_2 at the platinum-hydrogen electrode)

175

$E = -0.280 - 0.059\ \text{pH}$

(or, $\text{pH} = \dfrac{-0.280 - E}{0.059}$)

176

If the EMF of the cell just described is –0.280 volt when measured with a solution at pH 0 in contact with the platinum-hydrogen electrode, calculate the pH of another solution that under the same conditions yields an EMF of –0.782 volt.

pH = _____

This situation should help you in understanding both

1. why the pH scale for $[H^+]$ was so logical a development, and
2. how pH meters work.

(One ☐could ☐could not correctly introduce pH units directly on the voltage scale of the potentiometer, provided that the temperature remained constant.)

176

Since $E^0 = -0.280$ volt,

pH =

$\dfrac{-0.280 - (-0.782)}{0.059}$

pH = 8.5

could

177

Suppose that an electrical cell were constructed in which the two platinum-hydrogen half-cells of Item 176 were joined by a salt bridge. What potential difference could be observed between the platinum electrode dipping into the solution at pH 0 and that dipping into the solution at pH 8.5?

Answer: _____ volt, with electrode in the solution at pH 0 ☐positive ☐negative with respect to the other.

Such a cell that measures the potential arising from the difference in concentration of a single ion in two solutions is called a *concentration cell*. An oxidation-reduction reaction is in fact produced here also, namely a conversion of H^+ (1 M) to H_2 gas in the first half-cell, the electrons required being provided by the reverse process in the second half-cell. The difference between the two half-cells that drives the reaction is the difference in

_____.

$$-0.280 - (-0.782)$$
$$= +0.502 \text{ volt}$$

positive

The form of the Nernst equation applying to concentration cells for univalent cations at 25 °C is

$$E = 0.059 \log \frac{C_1}{C_2}$$

where C_1 and C_2 represent the concentrations of the ion and E is the potential of the electrode in the half-cell with concentration C_1.

(Note that $E^0 = 0$ in this case because the standard electrode reduction potentials for the two half-cells are identical.)

We will encounter in later items potential differences across membranes resulting from the difference in the concentrations of such ions as Cl^- or Na^+ in the two phases. Calculate the difference that would be observed with an appropriate electrode from the presence of K^+ at 150 mM on one side of membrane and at 5 mM on the other.

$[H^+]$

(the concentrations of the hydrogen ion)

Answer: _____ volt, the first phase being ☐electronegative ☐electropositive with respect to the second.

179

$$E = 0.059 \log \frac{150}{5}$$
$$E = 0.059 \log 30$$
$$E = 0.087 \text{ volt}$$

electropositive

MEMBRANE EQUILIBRIA

The Total Chemical Potential

180

✳ The arbitrariness with which systems must be described under the thermodynamic approach is nowhere more striking than in the study of biological membranes. We must define membranes having much simpler sets of properties than any real biological membranes; furthermore we shall consider almost exclusively the *equilibrium condition*, which is no more typical of membrane phenomena than it is of other biological behavior. Here, as much as in any area of biology, because it says nothing about rates of migration across membranes, the classical thermodynamic approach needs to be supplemented with the companion discipline that deals specifically with the rates at which events occur, namely _____ .

180

kinetics

181

✳ Nevertheless the conclusions reached by thermodynamics are decisive to the investigation and discussion of membrane phenomena. Unless we define the equilibrium condition for specified systems, we cannot expect, for example, to identify correctly the biological case in which *active transport* must be taken into account, nor to understand how it can be achieved and at what minimal cost in work.

Already, in Items 94 and 95, we developed the key concept needed for the present section: At equilibrium the chemical potential of any component across a membrane ☐ is constant ☐ shows a difference whose size depends on the nature of the two phases.   Recall from Item 92 that by a membrane we imply no more than an interface between two phases.

181

The full statement: At equilibrium the chemical potential of any component across a membrane is *constant* (although the activities may of course be different).

182

✳ We will restate this concept mathematically, using the subscripts 1 and 2 to identify the two phases and the subscript A to identify a component,

$$\mu_{1A} = \mu_{2A}$$

where the symbol μ stands for _____ _____.

＊ Of course, if the membrane is practically impermeable to a component (as is often the case in the biological context) it may take a very long time for the value μ_{2A} to reach μ_{1A}. Furthermore, if the concentrations of the components are in the meantime independently controlled by relatively rapid processes occurring on each side of the membrane, they may *never* become similar, even though the membrane is somewhat permeable to the component. Therefore, in spite of the thermodynamic prediction, equality of the chemical potential across the membrane can never be expected for such a component.

Does a similar limitation on thermodynamic predictions apply for chemical reactions? _____ .

the chemical
potential

183

Yes

184

✱ We need at this point to take into account the contribution to the chemical potential of two quantities not heretofore considered as variable. If a given quantity is constant throughout a system, we can include its effect in the value of μ_A; but differences often occur across membranes in the *pressure* and the *electrical potential*. These effects are described by the following equation for the *total chemical potential*, which we shall not derive at this point although a derivation may be found in Appendix C:

$$\mu_A^t = \mu_A + \overline{V}_A (P - P_0) + z_A F \phi$$

where $\mu_A = \mu_A^0 + RTln[A]$, as previously defined for a fixed pressure P_0, and no electrical potential. In this equation,

$\overline{V}_A$ is the molar volume of component A, i.e., the volume occupied by one mole. This quantity is usually measured as $\Delta V/\Delta n_A$ for the system, where Δn_A is small enough to avoid changing the rest of the system.*

ϕ the Greek letter *phi*, represents the electrical potential of the phase, usually measured with respect to some arbitrary zero point. The voltage across the membrane is the difference between the potential of the two phases.

z_A is the electrical charge on the A molecule.

F represents the _____ constant, as introduced in the preceding section.

*To be more exact we should write $\overline{V}_A = (\partial V/\partial n_A)_{P,T,n_B,n_C}\cdots$ (Recall the discussion of chemical potential in Items 88–89.)

185

✶ When the pressure or electrical potential is not uniform throughout the system, we must use μ_A^t rather than μ_A as defined here. The final term of this equation, $z_A F \phi$, disappears, however, for a molecule lacking net _____ .

　　We will now consider these two factors in sequence, first pressure differences, then potential differences.

Osmotic Pressure

186

✶ The significance of pressure differences to membrane phenomena relates particularly to movements of solvent and to the osmotic pressure.

　　In connection with our definition of the chemical potential we introduced the concept of the activity:

$$\mu_A = \mu_A^0 + RT \ln a_A$$

where a_A is the activity of A. We will now extend the concept of the activity also to the *solvent*, using the subscript s to designate it:

$$\mu_s = \underline{\hspace{2cm}} + RT \ln a_s$$

184

Faraday

185

charge

The full equation:

$$\mu_s = \mu_s^0 + RT \ln a_s$$

✱ We will consider the solvent in the pure state to be in its *standard state*, at which the activity $a_s = 1$. If we dissolve some substance in the solvent, a smaller proportion of the total number of molecules present will be solvent molecules. Therefore we can say that the *mole fraction* of the solvent has been decreased. As a consequence we observe a reduction in ☐the activity only   ☐the chemical potential only   ☐both the activity and the chemical potential   of the solvent.

✱ This observation of a reduced activity of the solvent might be made by noting a decreased tendency of solvent molecules to escape into the atmosphere; i.e., its vapor pressure would be decreased. Another method for observing a decreased *escaping tendency* is of particular importance to our subject. If we were to separate our solution from a quantity of the pure solvent by a membrane, as illustrated in the sketch, and if we were to specify that the membrane is permeable to the solvent but not to the solute (i.e., that it is semipermeable*) we should note that the escaping tendency of the solvent from the solution is lower than that from the pure solvent.

| I. Solution | 2. Pure Solvent |

The results would be an unbalance between the movements of solvent in the two directions, so that a net movement would occur from ☐left ☐right to _____. (Note that the term *escaping tendency* is a qualitative and intuitive concept. The *activity* is the rigorous term to be preferred.)

both the activity and the chemical potential (Item 186 specified how they change together.)

---

*Note that this term is given a precise meaning. It should not be used loosely to describe membranes permeable to some solutes and impermeable to others.

188

right, left

189

semipermeable

phase 1

activity (or chemical
potential)

190

$RT \ln a_{2s}$
(You are also cor-
rect if you wrote
zero or $RT \ln 1$,
since the activity
of the pure solvent
is 1.)

189

✱ Note that we need to consider only the solvent,
because we have specified that no other
molecules cross the membrane, since it is

_____.

We know experimentally that we can
stop this movement of solvent by applying
hydrostatic pressure on ☐phase 1 ☐phase
2. When we have exerted enough pressure
to stop all net migration of the solvent, the
system is in equilibrium, hence

$$\mu^t_{1s} = \mu^t_{2s}$$

The pressure difference we have produced
is just sufficient to compensate for the difference
in the _____ of the solvent.

190

✱ If we assume that there is no potential difference across the membrane, from the equation of Item 184 we can obtain, for equilibrium,

$$\mu^0_{1s} + \overline{V}_s (P_1 - P_0) + RT \ln a_{1s} =$$
$$\mu^0_{2s} + \overline{V}_s (P_2 - P_0) + \underline{\hspace{3cm}}$$

191

✱ Since the standard state for s is the same for
both phases, (i.e., $\mu^0_{1s} = \mu^0_{2s}$) and since the
value of a_{2s} is 1, we can simplify the equation
as follows,

$$P_1 - \underline{\hspace{2cm}} = -\frac{RT}{\overline{V}} \ln a_{1s}$$

192

✱ In the present case, where one of the two solutions separated by a membrane is pure solvent, the additional pressure that must be applied to the second solution to stop net solvent movement into it is known as its *osmotic pressure, Π*. Our equation thus becomes the equation for the osmotic pressure of a solution

$$\Pi = \underline{\hspace{3cm}}$$

The complete equation:

$$P_1 - P_2$$
$$= -\frac{RT}{\overline{V}_s} \ln a_{1s}$$

193

✱ The osmotic pressure is the pressure that must be applied to a solution to place it in an equilibrium of distribution with the pure solvent across a semipermeable membrane.* It is a property of the *solution* arising from the decreased activity of the *solvent*. Accordingly, the only role of the solute in the phenomenon of the osmotic pressure is

☐ 1. to reduce the mole fraction and therefore the activity of the solvent.

☐ 2. to exert a pressure itself by bombardment of the membrane.

The complete equation:

$$\Pi = -\frac{RT}{\overline{V}_s} \ln a_{1s}$$

*In the literature of plant physiology, the current trend is to use the term *osmotic potential, ψ_π*, (or *solute effect, S* or ψ_S) equal to $+(RT/\overline{V}_s) \ln a_s$, rather than the osmotic pressure. ψ_π is negative for solutions, and in the absence of pressure differences, solvent will move osmotically toward the more negative osmotic potential, i.e., the lower chemical potential. Note that the osmotic potential is just the negative of the osmotic pressure. See C. A. Price, *Molecular Approaches to Plant Physiology* (McGraw-Hill, New York, 1970) or F. B. Salisbury and C. Ross, *Plant Physiology* (Wadsworth, Belmont, Calif., 1970).

193

☑1. to reduce the mole fraction... (This choice is extremely important. For a reason we shall encounter later, there is a real temptation to associate the osmotic pressure with the *solute* rather than with the solvent.)

194

✳ Had we written the equation for two different solutions, rather than for the pure solvent and a solution, it would have taken the form,

$$P_1 - P_2 = - \frac{RT}{\overline{V}_s} \ln (a_{1s}/a_{2s})$$

Since Π is given for each of these solutions as follows,

$$\Pi_1 = - \frac{RT}{\overline{V}_s} \ln a_{1s}$$

and

$$\Pi_2 = - \frac{RT}{\overline{V}_s} \ln a_{2s}$$

we can write

$$\Pi_1 - \Pi_2 = - \frac{RT}{\overline{V}_s} \ln (a_{1s}/a_{2s})$$

Comparing this equation with the first one in this item, we see that

$$P_1 - P_2 = \Pi_1 \underline{\hspace{3cm}}$$

194

The complete equation:
$$P_1 - P_2 = \Pi_1 - \Pi_2$$

195

✳ Therefore the pressure difference that must be imposed to stop the flow of solvent from one solution to another across a _____ membrane is equal to the difference in the _____ pressures of the two solutions.

✳ Red blood cells normally contain a solution with an osmotic pressure of 8.4 atm, equal to that exerted by a 0.31 M sucrose solution, or a 0.155 M $NaCl$ solution. This means that if red blood cells were placed in distilled water

☐ 1. the external water because of its higher activity would tend to enter the cell, unless this osmotic pressure can be countered.

☐ 2. the internal solutes would exert a pressure of 8.4 atm on the interior surface of the red cell membrane.

semipermeable

osmotic

☑1. the external
water would tend
to enter the cell
unless...

✱ The increased internal pressure caused by such water entry can by no means be withstood by the red blood cell membrane; hence it will be stretched until holes are opened large enough for even the hemoglobin (molecular weight 65,000) to escape. This process is called *hemolysis*.

An algal cell with a similar internal osmotic pressure (8.4 atm) can grow in a dilute nutrient medium, with an osmotic pressure of only 1 atm, because the cell is surrounded by a rigid cell wall strong enough to resist the stretching caused by osmotic movement of water ☐into ☐out of the cell. Under these conditions, the cell develops a hydrostatic or *turgor* pressure (a pressure exerted against the wall from the interior). At equilibrium, the turgor pressure will be equal to the difference in the osmotic pressures of the cytoplasm and the nutrient solution, and there will be no net movement of water into or out of the cell. Calculate the turgor pressure under these conditions.

_____ atm

✳ If we should want to prepare a solution in which the red blood cell can be suspended without its tending to swell and perhaps be hemolyzed, we could dissolve 0.9 per cent *NaCl* in the water to obtain a suitable medium. This solution has the same osmotic pressure as the cell sap; that is, it is *isoosmotic* with the cell interior. Note that the solution within the cell is by no means 0.9 per cent *NaCl* in composition. We could equally well have used 0.31 *M* sucrose solution, as far as considerations of osmotic pressure apply. The role of the *NaCl* or of the sucrose in increasing the osmotic pressure is merely to decrease the _____ of the water in the suspending medium.

into

$$(8.4 - 1) = 7.4$$

✳ Other considerations do, however, introduce some caution in the choice of the solute used for this purpose. One might choose a substance (e.g., urea) that enters the cell almost as rapidly as the water does. Since the osmotic pressures of the cell interior and exterior would then be increased equally, the use of an isoosmotic solution of urea would cause ☐swelling and hemolysis ☐no change ☐cell shrinkage. From this behavior we can see that the membrane surrounding the red blood cell is not really a _____ membrane.

activity (or chemical potential)

swelling and
hemolysis

semipermeable

☑ 0.155 *M NaCl*

☑ 0.31 *M* sucrose

✱ We speak of a solution that can be brought into contact with cells or tissues without disturbing the distribution of water as *isotonic*. From what has been said, which of the following solutions would you judge to be both *isoosmotic* and *isotonic*?

☐ 0.155 *M NaCl*
☐ 0.31 *M* urea
☐ 0.31 *M* sucrose

✱ So far we have mentioned two methods for measuring the activity of the solvent in a solution, namely, observation of the vapor pressure of the solvent, and observation of the osmotic pressure of the solution. The vapor pressure of the solvent ☐ increases ☐ decreases as more solute is added, whereas the osmotic pressure of the solution

_____.

✱ Two other methods of measuring changes in activity of the solvent deserve mention because of their practical convenience. These are the observations of the *boiling point elevation* and of the *freezing point depression.*

Since for all of these determinations the action of the solute is merely to lower the _____ of the _____, the results obtained are independent of the nature of the solute or solutes used, and the four properties change together. For that reason the term *colligative properties of solutions* (colligative = sticking together) is often applied to these four properties, namely:

1. _____ ,
2. _____ ,
3. _____ ,
4. _____ .

Measure any one of them and you have a measure of them all.

decreases

increases (Note the negative sign in the equation of Item 192.)

202

activity, solvent

1. vapor pressure lowering
2. (appearance of) osmotic pressure
3. boiling point elevation
4. freezing point depression
   (in any order)

203

✱ We have seen that the osmotic pressure depends on the activity of the solvent:

$$\Pi = -\frac{RT}{\overline{V}_s} \ln a_s$$

An approximate equation developed by van't Hoff gives the osmotic pressure, remarkably enough, in terms of the molar concentration of *the solute*. It has the simple form $\Pi = RT[A]$, which looks deceptively like the ideal gas law, although it is nothing of the sort. We will develop this equation in the next four items for two reasons:

1. To warn the student against deciding, when he encounters this equation, that *the solutes* exert the osmotic pressure.* Such an equation is possible only because the solvent activity can be stated approximately in terms of solute concentration.

2. Because this approximate equation is used in determining the molecular weights of proteins by measuring the osmotic pressure.

The activity of a solute, as we have noted, becomes almost identical with its concentration at ☐low ☐high concentrations. Similarly, the *mole fraction* of the *solvent* has been found to be a suitable approximation of its activity for dilute solutions, the standard state of the solvent in that case being pure solvent.

*The view that solutes, by bombarding a membrane impermeable to them, can produce osmotic pressure has had considerable currency. See F. P. Chinard and T. Enns, Osmotic pressure. *Science 124,* 472–474 (1956) for an effective rebuttal.

The mole fraction of solvent, X_s, is given by

$$X_s = \frac{n_s}{n_A + n_B + n_C + \ldots + n_s}$$

where the terms n_A, etc., refer to the total numbers of moles of A, B, etc.

An equation similar to that for the mole fraction of solvent can of course be written for the mole fraction of each component; for example, (complete the equation)

$$X_A = \underline{\hspace{4cm}}$$

The full equation:

$$X_A = \frac{n_A}{n_A + n_B + n_C + \ldots + n_s}$$

We may note that the mole fractions of all components must add up to 1. Hence we may say that

$$X_s = 1 - (X_A + X_B + X_C + \ldots)$$

Furthermore, for dilute solutions, far larger numbers of solvent molecules than solute molecules are present. For example, for a liter of 0.1 M sucrose solution, $n_s = 55.4$, $n_A = 0.1$.

Therefore we can introduce the approximation, $X_A \simeq n_A/n_s$, and also the approximation, $V \simeq n_s \overline{V}_s$, in this case neglecting the contribution of the solutes to the volume. Hence we can write

$$X_A \simeq n_A/n_s \simeq n_A (\overline{V}_s/V) = \overline{V}_s[A]$$

In words, this equation permits us to say that the mole fraction of any solute is approximately the product of the partial molar volume of the solvent and the _____ in very dilute solutions.

We can of course write a similar expression for each solute, and when these expressions are all summated we can state the activity of the solvent in terms of the concentrations of the solutes, as follows

$$a_s \simeq 1 - \overline{V}_s \left([A] + [B] + [C] + \cdots\right)$$

From our fundamental definition of the osmotic pressure

$$\Pi = \underline{\hspace{4cm}}$$

we can write

$$\Pi \simeq -\frac{RT}{\overline{V}_s} \, ln \, [1 - \overline{V}_s \, (\underline{\hspace{2cm}})]$$

concentration of the solute
(molarity, molality)

We will now introduce one more approxima-tion.

In the expression, $- ln(1 - x)$, suppose that x is small, as follows:

If $x = 0.1$, then $- ln(1 - x)$
$$= - ln\ 0.9 = 0.105$$
If $x = 0.01$, then $- ln(1 - x)$
$$= - ln\ 0.99 = 0.0101$$
If $x = 0.001$, then $- ln(1 - x)$
$$= - ln\ 0.999 = 0.00100$$

We can see that $- ln(1 - x)$ is approximately equal to x for small values of x. If we make the corresponding substitution of

$$\overline{V}_s\ ([A] + [B] + [C] + \ . \ . \ .)$$
$$for$$
$$- ln\ \{1 - \overline{V}_s\ [A] + [B] + [C] + \ . \ . \ .\}$$

in the final equation of Item 206, we obtain

$$\Pi \simeq + RT(\underline{\hspace{3cm}})$$

The complete equa-tions:

$$\Pi = - \frac{RT}{\overline{V}_s}\ ln\ a_s$$

$$\Pi \simeq - \frac{RT}{\overline{V}_s}\ ln\ \{1 - \overline{V}_s([A] + [B] + [C] + \ . \ . \ .)\}$$

The approximate equation

$$II \simeq RT \ ([A] + [B] + [C] + \ . \ . \ . \ .)$$

derived in the preceding items is known as the *van't Hoff equation*.

A circumstance that makes us very cautious toward the van't Hoff equation is that, as we have mentioned, it appears to convince many students that the osmotic pressure is exerted by the *solute molecules* rather than by the *solvent molecules*. We have seen that the only basis for introducing solute concentration into the equation was to obtain an easy approximation for the activity of the _____.

The full equation:
$$\Pi \simeq \ + RT \ ([A] \\ + [B] + [C] \\ + \ldots)$$
(or, where A is the only solute,
$$\Pi = RT \ [A])$$
(Note that $\overline{V}_s$ cancels out.)

209

To use the van't Hoff equation in determining the molecular weight of proteins, first recall that if C_A is the concentration of A in grams per liter, and M_A is the molecular weight of A,

$$[A] = C_A/M_A, \quad \text{or} \quad M_A = C_A/[A]$$

If the only solute present is A, we can write, from the van't Hoff equation (complete the equation),

$$M_A = RT \underline{\hspace{3cm}}$$

solvent

Because of the several approximations used, M_A frequently is obtained for several protein concentrations, and the value extrapolated to $C_A = 0$.

Check back a few items: are all the approximations introduced in deriving the equation

$$\Pi = RT[A]$$

$$\text{from}$$

$$\Pi = -\frac{RT}{\overline{V}_s} \ln a_s$$

of such a nature as to become more nearly correct as C_A approaches zero? \underline{\hspace{1.5cm}}.

The following table shows the osmotic pressures observed for a protein at 3 concentrations in water solution at 25°C, and the reciprocals of the molecular weight calculated from the van't Hoff equation:

C_A	Π	$1/M_A = \dfrac{\Pi}{RTC_A}$
gm/liter	atm (found)	mole/gm (calculated)
0.50	0.00040	0.000033
1.00	0.00090	_____
2.00	0.00230	_____

Complete the table and plot the data on the following set of coordinate axes. In this case, to keep your units consistent, you should use $RT = 24$ liter-atm/mole, one of the values given in the table facing the back cover.

The full equation:

$$M_A = RT\,\frac{C_A}{\Pi}$$

Yes

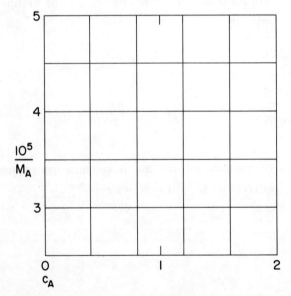

The best value of M_A is about _____ gm/mole.

210

$1/M_A$

mole/gm

0.000033

0.000038

0.000048

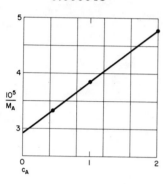

$10^5/2.9 = 35,000$

211

Note that if van't Hoff's equation applied precisely, all the calculated values for $1/M_A$ would be identical.

In that case, the line in this figure would be ☐ as drawn ☐ horizontal.

211

horizontal

Potential Differences;
the Gibbs-Donnan Equilibrium

212

✳ Having considered differences in pressure on
the two sides of a membrane in the last 20
items, we will next turn to effects of potential
differences across the membrane. The presence
of such a potential difference will influence
the distribution of all ions bearing a net charge.
To extend to the distribution of ions the
generalization that at equilibrium the chemical
potential of a component is constant across a
membrane, we need to include the electrical
term in our equation for the total chemical
potential

$$\mu^t_A = \mu_A + \overline{V}_A(P - P_0) + z_A F \phi$$

where z_A is the electrical ☐charge ☐po-
tential on the ion in question, F is the Faraday constant, and ϕ is the electrical potential
of the given phase.

212

charge

213

✳ When the electrical term thus makes a definite contribution to the *total chemical potential*, μ_A^t is frequently called the *electrochemical potential*.

Simply because we observe in a given case a net migration of K^+ *against its own concentration gradient,* to enter a phase that is negative by 10 millivolts relative to the phase from which the K^+ originates, we cannot conclude that *active transport* has occurred. First we must calculate the ☐chemical ☐electrochemical potential of K^+ in the two phases, to see whether the net movement of K^+ is really in the unexpected direction. Perhaps the difference in charge between the two phases is sufficient to account for the direction of K^+ movement.

214

✱ Let us consider then the case in which the membrane is permeable not only to the solvent but also to some of the ionic species present. Is this the kind of membrane we have defined as semipermeable? _____.

  First we will consider the situation that arises when the membrane is permeable to the ions of only one charge, let us say to the *anions*. We will suppose that Na^+ and Cl^- are the only ions present in the system pictured here, and that the salt concentration is *higher in phase 1*. We will suppose that sufficient pressure is applied on it to prevent migration of the solvent.

electrochemical

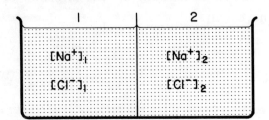

Cl^- will now show a tendency to move as a net from phase ☐1 ☐2 to phase _____.

215

✱ Does this mean that *no* chloride ions move in the opposite direction? _____.

No (See footnote to Item 188.)

1, 2

215

No (It is important to remember that large fluxes of Cl^- will occur in both directions; the two will be very nearly equal.)

216

✳ Only a very few chloride ions can move to the right in excess of the number moving to the left, however, before a potential difference is set up, sufficient to arrest further migration. The migration will nevertheless have the effect of making phase 1 more ☐negative ☐positive, and phase 2 more _____.

216

positive

negative

217

✳ We should emphasize again that only a very tiny proportion of the chloride ions have left phase 1 and entered phase 2, so that chemical analysis could not reveal a disparity between the $[Na^+]$ and the $[Cl^-]$ in phase 1, nor such a disparity in phase 2. This principle is the *principle of electroneutrality:* no potential difference achievable in practice is sufficient to cause a measurable difference in the total concentration of cations and in the total concentration of anions of a solution or phase, provided that each concentration is measured in ☐moles per liter ☐equivalents of charge per liter.

✳ In practical terms, this principle means that when the cations cannot move from one phase to another, the anions cannot either, to any measurable extent. Superficially, we might conclude that the anion permeability ought to be disregarded because it is of no consequence. But that very tiny net movement of Cl^- from phase 1 to phase 2 is just as important as the tiny donation of electrons that Cu^{++} can make to a copper electrode in an isolated half-cell. It gives rise to a potential difference that needs to be included to describe the system properly.

When we include the potential term for each phase, we obtain the following statement for the constancy of the chemical potential of chloride across the membrane:

$$\mu^t_{Cl_1^-} = \mu^t_{Cl_2^-}$$

or

$$\mu^0_{Cl^-} + RT\ ln[Cl^-]_1 + z_{Cl^-}\,F\phi_1$$
$$= \mu^0_{Cl^-} + \underline{\hspace{3cm}}$$

equivalents of charge
per liter

218

$$RT \ln [Cl^-]_2 + z_{Cl^-} F\phi_2$$

219

negative

lower

220

$$\phi_1 - \phi_2 =$$
$$-\frac{2.303}{F} RT \log \frac{0.01}{0.1}$$
$$= -0.059\ (-1)$$
$$= 0.059 \text{ volt}$$

219

* Rearranging, we obtain

$$\phi_1 - \phi_2 = \frac{RT}{z_{Cl^-} F} \ln \{[Cl^-]_2/[Cl^-]_1\}$$

Since z_{Cl^-} has a negative value, this equation confirms that the phase with the lower salt concentration will be the more ☐negative ☐positive. If the membrane were permeable to cations instead of anions, the phase with the ☐higher ☐lower salt concentration would be the more positive.

220

* If phase 1 contains 0.1 M $NaCl$, and phase 2, 0.01 M $NaCl$, calculate the potential difference across a membrane permeable to chloride only.

$$\phi_1 - \phi_2 = \underline{\hspace{2cm}} \text{ volt.}$$

221

Only when this potential difference is taken into account can we confirm that the chemical potential (more specifically the _____ _____ potential) of Cl^- is constant across the membrane at equilibrium.

✳ Next, let us give the membrane the property of holding back only part of the anions, being readily permeable to the solvent, to cations, and to all anions except those of one type. Here we encounter the *Gibbs-Donnan effect*.

We can obtain that situation easily by using a cellophane membrane to divide a *NaCl* solution into two compartments, and then introducing the sodium salt of a large anion, i.e., a macromolecule, into one of the compartments. (In the biological context the situation is usually more complex because even some of the small ions may have very little ability to pass through the membrane.)

Let us suppose we begin with *NaCl* at an equilibrium of distribution between two aqueous solutions as sketched.

electrochemical

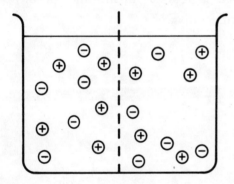

Since the two solutions are identical, and since we presuppose no potential or pressure difference across the membrane, the concentrations both of Na^+ and Cl^- ☐will be ☐need not be the same in the two compartments. The sketch is drawn to represent this situation.

✱ Now let us add to one compartment the Na^+ salt of a large polyvalent anion, say a sodium ribonucleate or a sodium albuminate, dissolved in a neglible amount of solvent. The polyanion cannot pass through the membrane.

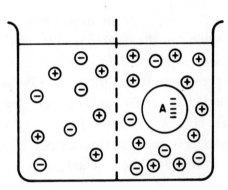

will be

The sketch shows five new sodium ions added along with one molecule of the pentavalent anion.

We may surmise that two effects should arise:

1. The activity of the water will have been reduced in the right-hand compartment. Hence water will tend to move from the ☐left ☐right to the _____ . We will suppose that a sufficient pressure is applied to prevent that movement. (Since $\overline{V}_{Na^+}$ and $\overline{V}_{Cl^-}$ are small, we will also assume that this increase in pressure has no effect on the chemical potential of the Na^+ and the Cl^- ions.)

2. The chemical potential of Na^+ in the right-hand compartment now obviously exceeds that of Na^+ at the left. Therefore Na^+ will tend to move from _____ to _____ .

224

223

✱ Even though the chloride ion concentration is initially constant across the membrane, as the Na^+ moves down the gradient of its chemical potential, the principle of electroneutrality requires that Cl^- must migrate at the same time in the ☐same ☐opposite direction.

left, right

right, left

This requirement means that as the Na^+ is moving in the direction of its concentration gradient, Cl^- will be moving so as to create a new concentration gradient. Obviously, the situation in which each of these ions has the same concentration on one side of the membrane as it does on the other ☐will soon ☐can never be reached.

same

can never

lower

The full equation:
$$\mu^t_{Cl^-} = \mu^0_{Cl^-} +$$
$$RT \ln [Cl^-]_1$$
$$- F\phi_1 = \mu^0_{Cl^-}$$
$$+ RT \ln [Cl^-]_2$$
$$- F\phi_2$$

✱ In the system described, the concentration of Na^+ will always remain higher and the concentration of chloride_____ in the phase containing the nondiffusible anion than in the other phase. To observe that the electrochemical potential of each of the two ions across the membrane is nevertheless constant at equilibrium, we must again include the potential term in our equation for the total chemical potential. For Na^+ we obtain

$$\mu^t_{Na^+} = \mu^0_{Na^+} + RT \ln [Na^+]_1 + z F \phi_1$$
$$= \mu^0_{Na^+} + RT \ln [Na^+]_2 + z F \phi_2$$

(We can simplify by omitting z because for Na^+ its value is $+1$.)

Write the corresponding equations for the electrochemical potential of the chloride ion in the two phases, noting carefully that its charge is minus *one*:

$$\mu^t_{Cl^-} = \underline{\hspace{5cm}}$$

$$\underline{\hspace{6cm}}$$

✱ We can further simplify these equations to obtain, for Na^+

$$\ln \frac{[Na^+]_1}{[Na^+]_2} = \frac{F(\phi_2 - \phi_1)}{RT}$$

and for Cl^-

$$\underline{\hspace{3cm}} = \frac{F(\phi_2 - \phi_1)}{RT}$$

227

* From these two equations it follows that at equilibrium

$$\frac{[Na^+]_1}{[Na^+]_2} = \frac{[Cl^-]_-}{[Cl^-]_-}$$ (Insert the subscripts into the second fraction.)

This relationship among the concentrations of the diffusible ions when one or more non-diffusible ions are present is known as the *Gibbs-Donnan* effect.

226

The full equation:

$$ln\frac{[Cl^-]_2}{[Cl^-]_1} = \frac{F(\phi_2 - \phi_1)}{RT}$$

(The detailed attention to the sign of z is tedious but necessary to our reaching of an important equation in one more step.)

228

* The larger the departure of these ratios (called the____________ - ____________ ratio) from unity, the ☐larger ☐smaller the Gibbs-Donnan effect, and the ☐higher ☐lower the relative concentration of the nondiffusible ion that has produced the effect.

227

The full equation:

$$\frac{[Na^+]_1}{[Na^+]_2} = \frac{[Cl^-]_2}{[Cl^-]_1}$$

228

Gibbs-Donnan

larger

higher

229

Yes

Yes

229

✳ Our diagram is presented again, but with a shift in the position of the ions to represent the attainment of equilibrium. Originally it showed five diffusible anions and five diffusible cations in each compartment. Check, have the Na^+ and the Cl^- migrated to the left in equivalent amounts?_____. Does our final diagram meet the conditions of the Gibbs-Donnan equilibrium that

$$\frac{[Na^+]_1}{[Na^+]_2} = \frac{[Cl^-]_2}{[Cl^-]_1} \, ? \underline{\hspace{2cm}}.$$

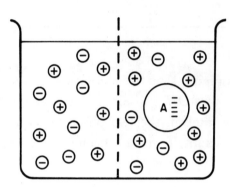

230

✳ Did the migration of Cl^- in reaching its equilibrium of distribution create a concentration gradient?_____.

We ☐will ☐will not call that behavior *active transport*, however, because this migration did not occur against a gradient of the ☐chemical ☐electrochemical potential of the chloride ion. This example illustrates well the necessity that thermodynamic considerations enter the description of transport.

231

Suppose that $NaHCO_3$ were also present in the system discussed in Items 222 to 230. Would the bicarbonate ion be expected also to participate in the redistribution, when the sodium salt of a nondiffusible anion is added?_____.

(Your response is related to a phenomenon encountered in CO_2 transport, called the *chloride shift*.*)

232

Assuming that the membrane is permeable to H^+ and OH^-, would you expect the pH to be the same in the two phases at equilibrium in the example we have been considering?_____.

233

* Use the equation of Item 219 to calculate the potential difference across the membrane generated at 25°C in the equilibrium diagramed in Item 229.

$\phi_1 - \phi_2 = $ _____

*See a learning program in this series, *Neutrality Control in the Living Organism* (W. B. Saunders Co., Philadelphia, 1971).

230

Yes

will not

electrochemical
(Although *chemical* is not strictly wrong, *electrochemical* is preferred.)

231

Yes (if the membrane is permeable to HCO_3^-)

232

No (These ions will assume corresponding asymmetries of distribution as determined by the potential difference between the two phases.)

233

$$(\phi_1 - \phi_2)$$
$$= \frac{2.303 \; RT}{-F} \log \frac{4}{6}$$
$$= 0.059 \times 0.176$$

$$\phi_1 - \phi_2 = 0.0104 \text{ volt}$$
(10.4 millivolts)

234

Yes

decrease

234

✱ When we examine the right-hand phase in the figure in Item 229, after Na^+ and Cl^- have migrated to an equilibrium distribution, we see that the nondiffusible particle represents one extra particle in that phase, creating a higher osmotic pressure through the lowering of the mole fraction of water.

Count the number of diffusible ions on the two sides of the membrane. Has the Gibbs-Donnan effect on the distribution of the diffusible ions increased the osmotic pressure difference? _____.

This effect will always be seen when one phase contains a higher level of nondiffusible anions than the other. If we can titrate the nondiffusible anions to their isoelectric state, the osmotic pressure difference will ☐increase ☐decrease.

235

✱ Living cells normally contain much higher concentrations of nondiffusible ions (mainly anionic macromolecules) than their environments. The result is a large Gibbs-Donnan effect, with the interior of the cell electronegative with respect to the external environment. Another consequence is that the interior of the cell would tend to have a ☐higher ☐lower osmotic pressure than the exterior, if small ions such as Na^+, K^+, and Cl^- were permitted to reach equal electrochemical potentials inside and outside the cell. As a result, water would tend to ☐leave the cell ☐enter the cell until it diluted infinitely the macromolecular anions.

235

higher

enter the cell until...

Active Transport

236

✳ Since most animal cells are not strong enough to oppose the resulting pressure of entering water, another mechanism had to be developed to counter this tendency, namely an extrusion of Na^+ against its electrochemical potential. Such a process is called an *active transport*.

What effect on the cell volume and cell integrity may be expected if this extrusion process is poisoned or is otherwise handicapped? _____ .

swelling and lysis
(or equivalent
words)
(Note that water
uptake can never
fully eliminate the
osmotic pressure
difference.)

A process by which Na^+ is specifically extruded from the cell would leave the K^+ free to respond to the potential difference across the plasma membrane and enter the cell spontaneously.

Qualitatively, this potential difference may appear to account for the high internal K^+ concentration characteristic of most cells.

We can investigate whether the effect of the potential difference is in fact sufficient, for example in the human red blood cell, by examining the distribution of the chloride ion, which as we have seen moves in and out of that cell freely. One finds under normal conditions that the ratio of $[Cl^-]$ in the plasma water to that in the cellular water is about 1.4:1. The direction of this asymmetry ☐corresponds ☐does not correspond to our expectation that the anionic hemoglobin inside the cell should produce a considerable Gibbs-Donnan effect.

We could apply the equation of Item 226 to calculate what electrical potential is indicated for the interior of the cell by this Cl^- distribution. Instead we can merely note directly that the ratio of $[K^+]$ in cellular water to $[K^+]$ in the plasma water has a very different value, namely about 30:1. It would require a very much larger potential difference than is revealed by the chloride analysis to account for that K^+ distribution. Hence we believe that K^+ ☐enters the cell spontaneously ☐is actively transported inward against its electrochemical gradient.

In agreement, the distribution of K^+ is easily disturbed by metabolic inhibitors or by cooling, that of chloride much less so.

corresponds

is actively trans-
ported . . .

The question whether the electrical potential difference is sufficient to explain the movement of an ion against its concentration gradient was also investigated for a transport process shown by frog skin. This process causes a transfer of Na^+ from the outside to the inside of the skin. The physiologists Ussing and Zerahn* showed that if two aqueous compartments were separated by a piece of frog skin, a potential difference was generated across the skin in the presence of Na^+. If an opposed current was applied just sufficient to cancel out this potential difference, no slowing of net Na^+ migration occurred. Indeed, the flow of current needed to neutralize the spontaneous potential difference was just equivalent to the quantity of Na^+ transported.

This result appears to mean that (select the best conclusion)

☐ 1. the net inward Na^+ movement was produced by the potential difference.

☐ 2. the net inward Na^+ movement was entirely unrelated to the potential difference.

☐ 3. the pumping of Na^+ appears to be the *source* rather than the *product* of the potential difference.

*H. H. Ussing and K. Zerahn, Active transport of sodium as the source of electric current in the short-circuited frog skin. *Acta Physiol. Scand.*, 23, 110 (1951).

Let us ask a theoretical question: Can a substance actually be caused to move as a net from a region of lower chemical potential to one of higher chemical potential, as we have just supposed for the sodium ion? This question comes to the core of the consequences of the Second Law of Thermodynamics for biology.

Maxwell imagined a device *(Maxwell's demon)* by which a path between two compartments could be opened only for the high-speed—hence the high-energy—molecules in a population of the molecules of a gas. In that way, a net movement might be produced against a gradient of pressure.

The response of thermodynamics to this proposition would be

☐ 1. that such an effect is quite likely to produce net movement of molecules against a gradient in an isolated system, since it is known that the molecules in a body of gas characteristically show a wide range of energies.

☐ 2. that the energy cost of operating such a device would be at least as great as that of the conventional way of increasing the pressure of a gas.

☑3. the pumping of Na^+ appears ...

240

☑2. that the energy cost. . .would be at least as great. . (Alternative 1 is excluded by the Second Law.)

241

✳ When we speak of active transport in this program, we understand that the energy producing the transport against the total chemical potential comes from some external source, not from the energy of the molecules themselves. Even then we exclude two ways in which the energy can come from outside.

It is clear that a *pressure differential* can cause a substance (usually the solvent) to move against its concentration gradient. But we have chosen to define the chemical potential broadly enough so that such pressure differences are ☐eliminated ☐taken into account.

We have seen that a *difference* in *electrical potential* can also cause a substance to move against a concentration gradient of that substance; but here also we have chosen to define the chemical potential broadly enough to ☐eliminate the potential difference ☐take into account its contribution to an enlarged concept of the chemical potential, the *electrochemical* potential.

✱ Other sources of asymmetry can exist, however, to cause a substance to migrate as a net against a gradient of the chemical potential by the broadest definition so far proposed. These can cause active transport.

Consider whether the following asymmetry represents such a case (see diagram):

Suppose that one molecule of the solute X and one sodium ion combine spontaneously at a site suitable for both, exposed on the surface of the plasma membrane. Suppose that this loaded site can then reorientate itself spontaneously toward the other surface of the membrane, so that Na^+ and X are both released into the cell interior. Suppose that this process can occur in either direction.

Suppose (quite plausibly) that the Na^+ concentration is 10 times as great in the exterior phase as in the interior phase.

Would it be a thermodynamically reasonable result that X should move into the cell until a considerable gradient of its chemical potential is created?_____ .

taken into account...

☑take into account its contribution...

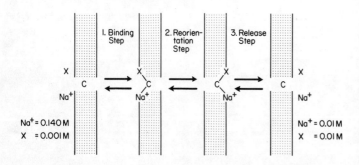

The shaded area in each diagram represents a plasma membrane, with the extracellular phase at the left and the cytoplasm at the right. A receptor site, C, for both the solute X and Na^+, is presented by a macromolecule, which is able to orientate itself first toward one and then toward the other phase.

242

Yes (Note that it is even possible that *all* the energy of the movement of Na^+ down its gradient can be conserved—i.e., that we have a *reversible* or *equilibrium* process.)

243

The migration of Na^+ in the direction of its concentration gradient.

No (Again, this would be excluded by the Second Law for an isolated system.)

243

✶ If so, what spontaneous process would be the immediate source of the energy of the active transport? _____

_____ . Could we say that Na^+ plus X, *considered together*, would move against their concentration gradients by this arrangement? _____ .

244

✶ The mechanism described in Item 242 is in fact pertinent to the active transport of amino acids and sugars. Of course it only shifts the question of the *primary* source of energy for transport one step farther back: "How then is Na^+ extruded from the cell against the gradient of its electrochemical potential?"

What thermodynamics can do is to set limits on how much can be achieved by coupling an energy-yielding process to a transport process. By equations of the type

$$\Delta G = 2.303 \ RT \log \{ [A]_2/[A]_1 \}$$

we can estimate the ☐minimal ☐maximal cost in energy of transferring a mole of A against a given gradient. Coupling it to a process yielding at least as much energy could solve the problem.

Note that we were able to omit ΔG^0 in this equation because we take the standard state of A to be the same in the two phases.

245

✱ Suppose for the purpose of argument that eventually we find that some contraction-relaxation cycle of protein structure causes a solute molecule to be grasped at one surface of the membrane, propelled across the membrane, and released at the other surface at a higher chemical potential. In the event that such a mode of operation should be the one actually found,

☐ 1. a *spontaneous* process would have been demonstrated by which molecules of a given species are brought from a lower chemical potential to a *higher chemical potential* in a closed system.

☐ 2. we may be sure that the process is driven by a certain *minimal amount of energy coming from outside the system as described.*

244

minimal (If the transfer is not achieved by a reversible process, the cost would be higher.)

245

☑2. we may be sure that the process is driven by . . . (If you approved the other proposition you have not understood the First Law. For an energy-requiring process to occur it must be coupled to an energy-yielding process.)

THE STEADY STATE. NONEQUILIBRIUM THERMODYNAMICS.

246

In the final 16 items of this program we will discuss some important extensions of thermodynamics to real processes. Sometimes in a sequence of reactions we find that some steps proceed at a state of equilibrium whereas others are not able to reach equilibrium. Even though the Ca^{++} and $PO_4^{\equiv}$ present in the solution *in vivo* may be approximately in equilibrium with respect to the bone with which they are in contact and the $PO_4^{\equiv}$ precisely in equilibrium with $HPO_4^{=}$ and H^+, nevertheless with respect to their incorporation into and release from the numerous other phosphorus-containing compounds of the organism, the concentrations of these two anions will probably not be at_____ , even though they are relatively constant with respect to time.

246

equilibrium

247

We call such a situation a *steady state*. In general a true state of equilibrium in metabolism is ☐characteristic of ☐incompatible with   life. Even in those cases in which we find two reactants in a living system in a state of equilibrium with each other, the concentration of one or both is almost certain to be in a_____ state, rather than in equilibrium, with respect to other processes and components of the system.

It is of course the relatively high speed of the reactions by which $PO_4^{\equiv}$ enters bone or reacts with H^+ to form $HPO_4^{=}$, compared to those by which it is incorporated into or released from organic phosphorus compounds, that permits the former reactions to approach or attain equilibrium, even though other related events in the biological context are not at equilibrium.

Let us consider still another case: Glycolysis proceeds normally in the living organism without of course bringing glucose and ethanol or lactate into equilibrium with each other. Normally, we would expect the concentrations of the various intermediates to be instead in a_____. Nevertheless, some of the steps in the glycolytic sequence can be shown to be at all times essentially at equilibrium. For example, aldolase permits the concentrations of hexose diphosphate and the triose phosphates to be at equilibrium with respect to the reaction it catalyzes. This circumstance requires that enough aldolase be present so that this reversible reaction is a relatively ☐fast ☐slow one in the sequence, i.e., so that it ☐is ☐is not *rate-limiting* to the process.

☐incompatible with

steady

(If you are at all familiar with the glycolytic sequence, from the information that the aldolase reaction is always at equilibrium, you might also conclude that the reaction ☐is ☐is not a point at which biological control is applied to glycolysis.)

steady state

fast

is not

249

is not
(Conversely, the presence of a large negative free energy change for a given step in a metabolic sequence at the concentrations that actually occur *in vivo* suggests that the step may be a point of control.)

250

former

250

Kinetics, the companion discipline to thermodynamics, has a special role of discovering for biological sequences which steps are at or near equilibrium and which steps in contrast are *rate-limiting.* For example, the principal way of simplifying *enzyme kinetics* has been to discover whether the first, key reaction, by which enzyme and substrate combine, establishes an equilibrium or a steady state. Only in the ☐former ☐latter case is classical thermodynamics fully applicable to that step.

251

Biological steady states are apt to be more complex than the examples of Items 246 to 249. In Item 242 we considered a case where the flow of Na^+ from a higher to a lower concentration was tightly coupled to the flow of X in the opposite direction. If no other pathway of movement were available, the two gradients of electrochemical potential might reach essentially the same finite value, but in the opposite directions. This result presupposes that the process pictured is thermodynamically

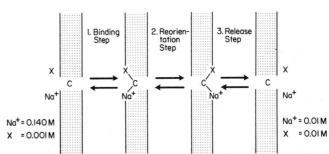

(Potential difference across membranes assumed to be 9 millivolts.)

We will picture another likely situation. First recall that normal cells maintain a gradient of Na^+ by an active extrusion process for this cation, which depends on ATP cleavage for energy. This so-called "ATPase pump" maintains a more or less constant gradient of Na^+, the Na^+ level being higher outside than inside the cell, despite a continuous flow of Na^+ into the cell through the type of cotransport system pictured in Items 242 and 251. (We will disregard for our example other kinds of Na^+ flow into the cell.) That cotransport system maintains in turn a fairly constant gradient of X in the opposite direction, this gradient being maintained despite a continuous flow of X from the cell through some kind of spontaneous leak.

Could we call the resultant situation an equilibrium?_____. Is the process described in this item thermodynamically reversible? _____. Is entropy produced by it?_____.

reversible

(The work done by migration of one Na^+ would be exactly equal to the work required to transport one X.)

252

No

No

Yes

253

☑ 1. A continuous input of energy is necessary...

253

A continuous input of energy accordingly is necessary for the process just described. Because of the constant flow of Na^+ through the device illustrated, this ion must constantly be pumped out of the cell to maintain the Na^+ gradient, and thus in turn maintain the gradient of X despite its constant flow by leakage from the cell. Check which of these two statements best describes the situation.

1. A continuous input of energy is necessary to maintain the steady state.

2. No energy is required because the concentrations are constant in time.

254

In the figure in Items 242 and 251 we supposed that the flow of Na^+ into the cell was tightly coupled to the flow of X in the same direction. Therefore, the situation could be described by a precise stoichiometry, like that of a chemical reaction:

$$Na^+_{out} + X_{out} \rightleftharpoons Na^+_{in} + X_{in}$$

Such tightness of coupling is very familiar to the biochemist, and in principle it would permit us to calculate how much work the flow of Na^+ will do. But instead the coupling may be incomplete, so that each Na^+ that enters through the system has only a *partial* tendency to bring an X molecule with it. Under this condition, will the flow of Na^+ into the cell perform work?_____. Will entropy be produced?_____. Why can't we calculate how much work the flow will perform using the Second Law of thermodynamics as we have so far applied it? _____

_____

255

254

It is rather fashionable to bring out the shortcomings of classical thermodynamics for the treatment of biological systems, which we say are virtually never at equilibrium. Yet many important reactions do proceed in an approximately reversible fashion in the living organism, and for those that do not, it is their departure from reversibility that we estimate. We are apt to be entirely at sea in understanding energy transfers unless we recognize and apply the limitations set by thermodynamics. Another kind of more complex procedure has been developed for analyzing processes not in equilibrium, for which the classical thermodynamic treatment leaves unanswered questions.

In Item 254 we supposed that two flows occurring in a single system are incompletely coupled. Approaches to the calculation of the work done and the entropy produced in such situations are contributed by the field of *nonequilibrium thermodynamics,* i.e., the *thermodynamics of irreversible processes.* We present here only a brief description of this approach.*

It is especially important to note that if two flows are occurring simultaneously during a given process, they need not both be flows of material; one or both of them may be the flow of a chemical reaction or a flow of electricity or of heat. One of the types of coupling of flows most interesting to us in biology occurs in biological transport, namely the coupling of the progress of a chemical reaction to the migration of a solute across_____.

Yes

Yes

(Any answers of the following sorts will serve:)

1. The process is irreversible.
2. Classical thermodynamics permits us only to determine the maximal work a flow can produce.
3. An unknown amount of energy released by the spontaneous migration of Na^+ is wasted.

---

* For a longer, yet relatively simple, discussion of this topic, see D. C. Spanner, *Introduction to Thermodynamics* (Academic Press, New York, 1964), Chapter 15. A more detailed analysis will be found in A. Katchalsky, and P. F. Curran, *Nonequilibrium Thermodynamics in Biophysics* (Harvard University Press, Cambridge, Mass., 1965).

255

a membrane

256

the solute from one phase to the other (or equivalent words)

256

We recognize that any given flow is driven predominantly by a particular force. Thus, the flow of heat is driven by the temperature difference, the flow of electrical current by the potential difference and the diffusion of matter by the gradient of the chemical potential. The force characteristically responsible for a flow is known as its *conjugate force*. Thus, the difference in the chemical potential of a solute in two phases is the conjugate force producing the flow of_____

_____.

257

We can write a generalized equation linking a flux, J, to its conjugate force, X, as follows:

$$J_1 = L_{11} X_1$$

where the proportionality constant L may be called a coupling coefficient. This equation generalizes Ohm's law for the flow of electricity, Fourier's law for the flow of heat, and so on. The two subscripts 1 and 1 mean that L_{11} links J_1 to X_1.

If we want to represent a different flow, J_2, occurring in the same system as a result of the force X_2, we may write the corresponding equation:

$$J_2 = \underline{\qquad}$$

These two equations imply that the two flows are independent of one another. But in the real situation, some of the energy released by one of these flows may be made available to the other. For example, a flow of heat from a warmer to a colder part can cause a flow of electricity and vice versa; and electric current can cause flow of solvent, a pressure on one part of a system can cause the flow of electricity, and so on. We may say that the flow is determined not only by its *conjugate force* but also by one or more *nonconjugate forces*. We can with certain reservations write for the first flow,

$$J_1 = L_{11} X_1 + L_{12} X_2$$

and for the second flow,

$$J_2 = L_{21} X_1 + \underline{\hspace{3cm}}$$

(The complete equation)

$$J_2 = L_{22} X_2$$

The complete equation:

$$\cdot J_2 = L_{21} X_1 + L_{22} X_2$$

The new feature of these formulations is the presence of the two *cross-coefficients*, L_{12} and L_{21}. If these coefficients are larger than zero, coupling between the flows takes place. A maximal value for the cross-coefficients representing tight coupling can be defined.

It was Onsager who showed in 1931 that such pairs of cross-coefficients as L_{12} and L_{21} must be equal. In words, Onsager's *reciprocity theorem* says, "When the flux J_i corresponding to an irreversible process is influenced by the conjugate force X_k applying for another process k, then the flux J_k is also influenced by the conjugate force X_i through the same coupling coefficient L_{ik}." Or more simply, if two flows interfere with each other, the interference will be the same in each direction.

In the system described in Items 242 and 251, could a flow arising from an independently maintained gradient of X serve to concentrate Na^+ into the phase at the right?_____. Given that a chemical reaction as it progresses can drive an active transport process, could the spontaneous flow of the transport substrate through that process cause the reversal of the chemical reaction?_____.

You may well use this concept when you study coupling of electron transport to oxidative phosphorylation in the mitochondrion.

Typically equations of the type illustrated in Item 257 show more than one nonconjugate force influencing a flow. The equations may be written in a form summating all forces affecting the flow,

$$J_i = \sum_{j=1}^{n} L_{ij} X_j$$

Although these equations can be derived from the equations of classical thermodynamics for the gain of entropy, the extension of their linear character to rapid processes and to points substantially removed from equilibrium is only a postulate. In addition, the cross-coupling coefficients are used without concern for the nature of the interaction between the flows. These equations are accordingly known as *phenomenologic* equations. Once the values for L_{ij} are known for a system over a given range of conditions, it becomes possible to calculate both the efficiency of the energy transfer and the rate of entropy production over that range. The chief lesson of these equations for us here lies in the concept of loose or incomplete coupling between two or more_____.

This idea means that even though no single flow may provide enough energy to drive a given flow, two or more flows together may supply sufficient energy.

Yes

Yes

(Both cases are qualitative examples of reciprocity in coupling.)

flows (or fluxes)
(Note that the coupling is *not* between the *gradients*.)

Below are listed a number of descriptions of systems in which two flows are occurring simultaneously. Check the cases in which you believe calculations of coupling between the flows could be usefully applied:

☐1.
  a. Heat is flowing from a part of a liquid that is being warmed to a part that is being cooled.
  b. Molecules of the liquid are diffusing from the second part to the first part because of a pressure difference.

☐2.
  a. An electrical current is made to flow from one part of a fluid to another.
  b. The molecules of the fluid are diffusing from the second part to the first part because of a pressure difference.

☐3.
  a. Water is flowing in the vascular system of a plant.
  b. Nutrients are flowing in the same vascular system.

☐4.
  a. ^{14}C-labeled glucose is being converted to ^{14}C-labeled CO_2 by a bacterial suspension, the amounts of both present being constant with time.
  b. All the ^{14}C present in the system is undergoing radioactive decay.

262

Returning finally to the contribution made by classical thermodynamics, let us suppose that a given biological process does not approach equilibrium in the biological context. Perhaps by studying the process *in vitro* we can determine where the equilibrium position, if it were attained, would lie. By that means we ☐can, nevertheless, ☐cannot, however, learn what *minimal* quantity of work is required to drive the process in the endergonic direction *in vivo*.

261

☑1. (thermo-osmosis)

☑2. (electro-osmosis)

☑3.

☐4. (On the basis of prior information you would presumably not expect any coupling between these flows.)

263

Since the overall biological processes go on and on under steady-state rather than under equilibrium conditions, the total free energy change during life has to be ☐positive ☐negative. The energy released to maintain these inherently inefficient nonequilibrium processes generally ☐is ☐is not available for biosynthetic processes. This is the reason that the organism needs a continuous input of available energy.

262

can, nevertheless (that minimum being approached as thermodynamic reversibility is approached)

263

negative

is not

SUMMARY

264

✱ Work and heat are the two forms in which
_____ is exchanged between systems.
The increase in total energy of a system is
determined by the amount of _____
absorbed by the system, plus the _____
done on the system by its surroundings.
Mathematically, we can write this statement as
follows:

$$\Delta U \underline{\hspace{4cm}}$$

(Items 7 to 21)

264

energy

heat

work

The full equation:
$$\Delta U = Q + W$$

265

✱ When a system undergoes a change of state, the
amounts of _____ and of _____
exchanged with the surroundings will depend
on the pathway followed, whereas the change
in _____ is independent of
the pathway. Thus the First Law tells us
that energy ☐ is continually being created
☐ can be destroyed during a change in state
☐ can be neither created nor destroyed.
(Items 17 to 21)

266

✱ We know also that ☐heat ☐work is less useful than other forms of energy, because it cannot be converted completely into_____.

　　This statement is ☐another form of the First Law ☐a statement of the Second Law of Thermodynamics.

　　(Items 36 to 38)

267

✱ Consider the following statement: The Second Law means that a description of a process in terms of the total energy change of the system is inadequate; we need to evaluate separately the heat and the work transferred into and out of the system. That statement is ☐strictly correct ☐unwarranted.

　　(Items 34 to 78)

268

✱ Proceeding then to evaluate the work and the heat separately, we know that when a change occurs along a thermodynamically reversible and isothermal pathway, the work required will be ☐maximal ☐minimal. If a process occurs in such a way that both the system and its surroundings can be returned to their original state, it is said to be_____.

　　(Item 45)

265

heat (Q), work (W)
　(either order)

(total) energy (U)
(also free energy, etc.)

☐can be neither created nor destroyed

266

heat

work

a statement of the Second Law

267

strictly correct

268

minimal

reversible

269

Under these conditions we can measure also the additional thermodynamic quantity,_____, which is equal to Q_{rev}/T. Can we also measure this quantity by determining Q/T for an irreversible change?_____.

(Items 53 to 62)

269

ΔS (entropy change)

No

270

✱ One well-known conclusion from the Second Law is that the entropy always ☐increases ☐remains constant ☐decreases during any spontaneous process occurring in an isolated system. Another important use of ΔS is to calculate the change in *free energy* from ΔH (which is usually equal to ΔU in biological systems). For this purpose we use the equation

$$\Delta G = \Delta H - T\Delta S.$$

This equation tells us that the increase in the work a system can do is generally ☐greater ☐less than we might suppose from the increase in its total energy (or enthalpy) by an amount measured by the gain in _____ by the system during the change.

(Items 63 to 66; Items 73 to 80)

271

✻ Which of the following quantities is equal to ΔG? (Check one or more.)
- ☐ 1. The minimal work that must be done on the system during a change.
- ☐ 2. The work that is done on the system during a reversible change.
- ☐ 3. The work actually done on the system in any process.
- ☐ 4. The heat absorbed by the system in a reversible process.

    (Items 42 to 49)

272

✻ To obtain a measure of the natural or spontaneous direction of a process we found that we could use these concepts of entropy and free energy. One does not have a reliable criterion as to whether a process will tend to occur spontaneously or not in the sign of ☐ ΔU ☐ ΔG, whereas the sign of _____does give us a reliable criterion, providing that temperature and _____are constant.

    (Items 49 to 52; Items 80 to 82)

270

increases

less

entropy

271

☑1. ⎫ (Remember that
        ⎬ if it is to require
        ⎪ only the minimal
☑2. ⎭ work the change
           must be reversible.)

272

☑ΔU

ΔG

pressure

273

spontaneously, al-
though we cannot
predict. . .

$\Delta G = -nFE$

not be spontaneous

274

equilibrium

273

✱ Any process for which ΔG is negative will tend to occur ☐spontaneously and readily ☐spontaneously, although we cannot predict whether or not the rate will be perceptible. Since the relationship between ΔG and the electrical potential, E, is given by the equation

$$\Delta G = \underline{\hspace{3cm}}$$

any oxidation-reduction reaction for which E is negative will ☐also tend to occur spontaneously ☐not be spontaneous.
(Items 49; 132 to 134)

274

✱ When G for a system reaches a minimum, a state of _____ has been reached.
(Item 50)

275

✱ If a reaction occurs with a sufficiently large free energy decrease, it can serve to drive another reaction, provided that the free energy increase of the second reaction is not algebraically ☐larger ☐smaller and provided that the two reactions are _____, i.e., that they share a component.
(Items 49, 123, 124)

276

* The chemical potential, μ, of a component of a system is defined in words as the change in the free energy of the system occurring with a change of ______________________________

______________________________.

(Items 85 to 91)

275

larger

coupled (linked)

277

When a substance has the same total chemical potential across a membrane, it is at an ______________ of its distribution.

(Items 95 to 97; 181 to 185)

276

one mole in the amount of the component (or similar words)

278

* We can relate the chemical potential of a component, *A*, to its concentration by the following approximate equation:

$$\mu_A = \underline{\hspace{4cm}}$$

A similar but precise equation serves to define a quantity somewhat similar to the concentration:

$$\mu_A = \underline{\hspace{4cm}}$$

This quantity is known as the ____________ of the component.

(Items 101 to 104)

277

equilibrium

278

The full equations:

$$\mu_A = \mu_A^0 + RT \ln [A]$$

$$\mu_A = \mu_A^0 + RT \ln a_A$$

activity

279

The full equation:

$$\mu_s = \mu_s^0 + RT \ln a_s$$

the pure solvent

280

The full equation:

$$\Delta G = \Delta G^0$$

$$+ RT \ln \frac{[E]^e \times [F]^f}{[A]^a \times [B]^b}$$

279

✱ Rewrite the latter equation as it applies to the chemical potential of the solvent.

$$\mu_s = \underline{\hspace{3cm}}$$

What do we take as the standard state of the solvent? That is, in what state does the activity of the solvent equal 1? _____ .

(Items 186 to 190)

280

✱ The equation that states the change in free energy of a chemical reaction,

$$aA + bB \longrightarrow eE + fF,$$

at any set of concentrations of the reactants and products is

$$\Delta G = \underline{\hspace{1.5cm}} + \underline{\hspace{3cm}}$$

(Items 106 to 112)

281

✱ The equation that states the relationship between the standard free energy change of a reaction and the equilibrium constant of the reaction is

$$\Delta G^0 = \underline{\hspace{3cm}}$$

(Items 111 to 116)

282

If we know the free energy of the formation (ΔG_f^0) of glucose from C, H_2 and O_2 and also that of fructose from the same elements, how can we obtain ΔG^0 for the conversion of glucose to fructose? _____

_____

(Items 117 to 121)

283

✱ In order to measure the tendency of a reaction to occur by observing the electromotive force it can generate, the following conditions must be met:

   (a) It must be a(n)_____
        reaction, i.e., one in which electrons
        are transferred.
   (b) The two parts of the reaction must be
        made to occur in two separate vessels
        called_____.
   (c) We must have electrodes that can

_____

(Items 132 to 165)

281

The full equation:
$$\Delta G^0 = -RT \ln K'_{eq}$$
(or $\Delta G^0 = -RT$
$$\ln \frac{[E]_{eq}^e \times [F]_{eq}^f}{[A]_{eq}^a \times [B]_{eq}^b}$$)

282

Obtain the difference
ΔG_f^0 (fructose)
   $- \Delta G_f^0$ (glucose)
(or equivalent
   words)

283

oxidation-reduction

half-cells

receive electrons
    from one half-cell
    reaction and trans-
    fer them to the
    other (or equiv-
    alent words)

284

✱ Fundamentally and for precision, the osmotic pressure of a solution should be stated in terms of the logarithm of the activity of the ☐solute, a_A,   ☐solvent, a_S,   according to this equation (complete):

$$\Pi = \boxed{\; - \; \dfrac{}{\overline{V}_s} \; ln \; a_s \;}$$

(Items 187 to 195)

284

solvent, a_s,

The full equation:
$$\Pi = -\frac{RT}{\overline{V}_s} ln \; a_s$$

285

✱ The osmotic pressure of a solution is the pressure that must be applied to it to place it in an equilibrium of distribution with the pure _____ across a _____ membrane.

(Item 193)

285

solvent

semipermeable

286

✱ The only role of the solute in the generation of the osmotic pressure is to _____

_____

The van't Hoff equation is able to provide ☐an approximation   ☐a precise statement of the osmotic pressure in terms of the concentration of any and all solutes, because for dilute solutions the activity of the solvent is given ☐approximately   ☐precisely   by the total concentration of solutes.

(Items 203 to 208)

287

✳ The relationship between the concentration of a diffusible anion, A^-, and that of a diffusible cation, B^+, in the Gibbs-Donnan equilibrium between two phases is given by this equation:

_____

(Items 225 to 229)

288

✳ The following equation

$$\phi_1 - \phi_2 = \frac{RT}{z_B F} \ln \frac{[B^+]_2}{[B^+]_1}$$

indicates that an electrical potential difference arises when ☐ a concentration difference of a diffusible ion is generated across a membrane ☐ a chemical reaction is occurring.
(Item 219)

289

✳ Life processes require that certain solutes be transferred across biological membranes against their electrochemical potentials. This process is called *active transport*.

Is that process inherent in the attainment of the Gibbs-Donnan equilibrium? _____.

On thermodynamic grounds, we know that the system in which such a process occurs can not be a(n) ☐ open ☐ closed ☐ isolated system; energy must be obtained from an outside source.

(Items 230; 236 to 245)

286

decrease the activity (mole fraction) of the solvent

an approximation

approximately

287

The full equation:
$$\frac{[B^+]_1}{[B^+]_2} = \frac{[A^-]_2}{[A^-]_1}$$

288

a concentration difference of a diffusible ion. . .

289

No

isolated

290

irreversible

291

active

☑may also

290

✴ The main overall metabolic reactions proceed under thermodynamically ☐reversible ☐irreversible conditions, so that a continuous input of available energy is needed to maintain a steady state.
(Item 263)

291

Thermodynamics emphasizes the essential similarity in the flow represented by the progress of a metabolic reaction and the flow of a metabolite across a biological membrane. If these flows are coupled so that the first makes part of its energy available to the second, the kind of transport called_____ transport can result. The linkage between these processes ☐may also ☐will not, however, permit energy to be transferred in the opposite direction, so that the flow of the metabolite across the membrane can cause advance of the chemical reaction.
(Item 259)

APPENDIX A

Examination Questions

(We recommend that this examination be used after each full perusal of the program to determine if all or parts of the program require further study.)

Objective Items

Below will be found two categories marked *A* or *B*, followed by the words *both* and *neither*. These are followed by a short series of numbered statements or phrases. In the parentheses preceding each numbered item, place an *A* or a *B* if only category *A* or category *B* pertains to that item. If *both* category *A* and category *B* pertain to the item, insert instead the letter *C* in the parentheses. If *neither A* nor *B* pertains, insert the letter *D* in the parentheses.

First Set:

    A. The First Law of Thermodynamics
    B. The Second Law of Thermodynamics
    C. Both
    D. Neither

(   )   1.   Concerns itself with transfers of heat and the performance of work.
(   )   2.   Is sufficient by itself for describing energy transfers in purely mechanical processes involving no heat transfer.
(   )   3.   Indicates which processes will proceed quickly and which will not proceed at all.
(   )   4.   Predicts the direction taken by chemical reactions.
(   )   5.   Is a statement of the law of the conservation of energy.
(   )   6.   Declares the nonequivalence of heat to other forms of energy.
(   )   7.   Shows that as objects come to have more and more the same temperature and similarly random composition and structure, it will become harder and harder to get work done.

Second Set :

    A. Spontaneity of a process

    B. Thermodynamic reversibility of a process

    C. Both

    D. Neither

(   ) 8. Unequivocally established, when ΔG for the system has a negative value under isothermal conditions.

(   ) 9. Unequivocally established, when ΔS for the system has a negative value.

(   ) 10. Unequivocally established, when maximal work is done by the process.

(   ) 11. Illustrated by the uncomplicated net migration of a solute from a phase in which its chemical potential is high to one in which its chemical potential is low.

(   ) 12. Only under this condition can ΔS be determined from the heat transferred.

(   ) 13. For the case in which one biochemical process drives another, this feature implies that the coupling is exceedingly efficient.

Third Set:

    A. ΔU

    B. ΔG

    C. Both

    D. Neither

(   ) 14. When a system undergoes a change of state, the value of this property does not depend on the pathway followed from one state to the other.

(   ) 15. Is divided between two components, *the heat transferred* and *the work done*.

(   ) 16. Specifically excludes the heat transferred under conditions such that heat transfer is maximal (or reversible) at constant temperature.

(   ) 17. If its value for a given process is negative under isothermal conditions, the process will certainly be a spontaneous one.

(   ) 18. Specifically measures the degree of order in a system.

(   ) 19. Has a value of zero at equilibrium.

(   ) 20. May be used to determine whether one reaction provides enough energy to drive another reaction with which the first is coupled.

(   ) 21. Includes only energy that can be made to do work, at constant temperature.

Fourth Set:

    A. ΔG

    B. ΔG^0

    C. Both

    D. Neither

(   ) 22.   Is equal to $-RT$ times the natural logarithm of the equilibrium constant of a reaction.

(   ) 23.   For an oxidation-reduction reaction, it is equal to $-n\mathcal{J}$ times the standard electrode reduction potential of the reaction.

(   ) 24.   If its value for a change in the state of a system is *zero,* the change will be spontaneous.

(   ) 25.   Is equal to $\Delta H - T\Delta S$ at constant temperature.

(   ) 26.   For a chemical reaction, it is expressed for 1 mole of the reaction, as the chemical equation is written.

(   ) 27.   For a chemical reaction, it is equal to the sum of the chemical potentials of the products, minus the chemical potentials of the reactants, each times the number of the moles of the component that participate in the reaction.

(   ) 28.   For a chemical reaction, it is independent of the concentration of the several components.

(   ) 29.   By *active transport* we mean that in an isolated system its value is positive.

Fifth Set:

    A. The chemical potential of the solute

    B. The chemical potential of the solvent

    C. Both

    D. Neither

(   ) 30.   Equals RT times the natural logarithm of the activity of this component.

(   ) 31.   Is precisely equal to μ^0 for that component, plus RT times the natural logarithm of the activity of that component.

(   ) 32.   At equilibrium, its value, defined in inclusive terms, is constant across a membrane.

Sixth Set:

    A. The activity of a component

    B. The chemical potential of a component

    C. Both

    D. Neither

(   ) 33. Is given by the concentration multiplied by the activity coefficient.

(   ) 34. For a chemical reaction, we can calculate ΔG if we know the value of this function for all components under the selected conditions, given that ΔG^0 is also known.

(   ) 35. ΔG for a chemical reaction is obtained by adding the values of this function for the products, and subtracting the value of it for the reactants, each times the number of the moles of the component that participate in the reaction.

(   ) 36. The osmotic pressure of a solution increases as the natural logarithm of this function for the solvent decreases from the unit value attributed to the pure solvent.

(   ) 37. For a solute, it is constant across a membrane at the equilibrium of distribution of the solute.

Seventh Set:

    A. ΔG

    B. E

    C. Both

    D. Neither

(   ) 38. Its sign gives a reliable indication as to the spontaneity of an oxidation-reduction reaction.

(   ) 39. A standard value for this function of a chemical reaction is determined with all components in specified standard states.

(   ) 40. By the accepted biochemical convention, a positive sign for this property of a chemical reaction, under any given set of conditions, indicates that the reaction will tend to proceed spontaneously and can presumably be made to do work.

(   ) 41. Is called *the standard electrode reduction potential.*

(   ) 42. From it, determined for a known set of concentrations of all components, we can calculate the equilibrium constant of a reaction, applicable at that same temperature.

Eighth Set

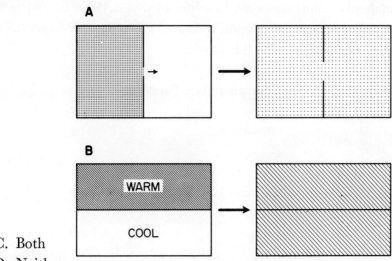

C. Both

D. Neither

The diagrams show two isolated systems, (*A*) two compartments connected by an orifice, and (*B*) two metal blocks in contact with each other. In the first case the molecules distribute themselves randomly between the compartments. In the second case the flow of heat from one block to the other brings them to the same temperature.

(   ) 43.   The process changes the enthalpy.

(   ) 44.   The process decreases the Gibbs free energy.

(   ) 45.   The process increases the entropy.

(   ) 46.   Under the given conditions the change can in some cases be made to proceed in the opposite direction.

Answers to objective items:

1. (C)	13. (B)	25. (A)	36. (A)
2. (A)	14. (C)	26. (C)	37. (B)
3. (D)	15. (A)	27. (A)	38. (C)
4. (B)	16. (B)	28. (B)	39. (C)
5. (A)	17. (B)	29. (D)	40. (B)
6. (B)	18. (D)	30. (D)	41. (D)
7. (B)	19. (B)	31. (C)	42. (C)
8. (A)	20. (B)	32. (C)	43. (D)
9. (D)	21. (B)	33. (A)	44. (C)
10. (B)	22. (B)	34. (C)	45. (C)
11. (A)	23. (B)	35. (B)	46. (D)
12. (B)	24. (D)		

Mathematical Problems

1. Consider 1 mole of a solute dissolved in 1 liter of water. What is the free energy change of the solute when this solution is diluted at $25°C$ with 9 liters of water? Assume activity coefficients equal 1.

2. Consider this reaction scheme for an isolated system.

$$A \xrightarrow[\text{cal/mole}]{\Delta G^0 = 2100} B \xrightarrow[\text{cal/mole}]{\Delta G^0 = -2700} C$$

A with $\Delta G^0 = 4100$ cal/mole $\downarrow E$

What is the value of ΔG^0 for conversion of A to C? of E to B? If any needed catalysts are present, would you expect conversion of E to B? of A to C?

3. The equilibrium constant for the dissociation of acetic acid, $[H^+] [OAc^-]/[HOAc]$, is $2 \times 10^{-5} M$ at $25°C$. This constant is frequently used in the form of its negative logarithm to the base 10, namely the pK', which equals 4.70. The prime mark signifies that concentrations rather than activities are used in its determination, which means that a given value will apply accurately only over a narrow range of total concentration or ionic strength of the solution.

    Calculate the value of ΔG^0 and $\Delta G'$ for the dissociation. Will dissociation be spontaneous at pH 1? At pH 7? Calculate the value of ΔG for pH 4.70. At what pH is the reaction at equilibrium if $[HOAc] = [OAc^-]$? Does this pH value depend on the total concentration, $[HOAc] + [OAc^-]$?

4. The solubility of crystalline picric acid (molecular weight, 229) in water at $25°C$ is 1.40 gm per kg solvent, and in ether, 2.00 gm per kg solvent. Calculate the standard free energy for the transfer of 1 mole of picric acid from water solution to ether solution, using molalities as concentration units and neglecting deviation of activity coefficients from unity. (The same problem may be considered for benzoic acid, soluble in water to 0.0218 molal and in ether to 4.54 molal.)

5. Frequently one can measure the standard electrode reduction potential of a compound without direct coupling to an electrode suitable to the substance. For example, suppose one adds a mixture of $K_3Fe(CN)_6$ and $K_4Fe(CN)_6$ to a mitochondrial suspension so that a ratio of $[Fe(CN)_6^{-4}]/[Fe(CN)_6^{-3}] = 2/1$ is

obtained. Suppose further he observes at equilibrium that cytochrome a in the mitochrondria becomes 11.5 per cent reduced.

(a) Calculate $E'_{1/2}$ for cytochrome a, assuming that pH $= 7$ and T $= 25°$C.

(b) Would the ferrocyanide-ferricyanide couple be useful for measuring the potential of cytochrome b_2, $E'_{1/2}$ about $+0.12$ volt?

6. The renal tubule is considered to be permeable to NH_3 but not to NH_4^+. Suppose that $[H^+]$ is 4×10^{-8} N on the periplasmic side (outside the tubule), whereas through the activity of the H^+ pump it is 4×10^{-5} N in the distal tubular urine (inside the lumen). Take the equilibrium constant $\dfrac{[NH_3] \times [H^+]}{[NH_4^+]}$ to be 4×10^{-10} in both phases. If $[NH_3] = 5 \times 10^{-7}$ M in both phases, how large a distribution ratio, $\dfrac{[NH_4^+]_{urine}}{[NH_4^+]_{plasma}}$ can be generated? What is the source of the energy for producing this gradient?

7. R. Kraayenhof [*Biochim. Biophys. Acta 180*:213 (1969)] has reported that under optimal conditions, isolated spinach chloroplasts are able to phosphorylate *ADP* to *ATP* in the light at pH 7.60 and 25°C to the extent that the following apparent equilibrium concentrations are reached: *ATP*, 138 μM; *ADP*, 5 μM; inorganic phosphate *(P_i)*, 670 μM. The energy for this phosphorylation comes from light-driven photosynthetic electron transport through cytochromes and other electron carriers, and at apparent equilibrium the free energy released in electron transport would exactly equal the free energy required to phosphorylate the *ATP*.

(a) What is the free-energy change for the formation of *ATP* at pH 7.60 and at the concentrations stated above? Use the value of 9.25 kcal/mole for the *standard* free-energy change at pH 7.60 and the magnesium concentration used in these experiments.

(b) What minimum oxidation-reduction potential difference between adjacent electron transfer chain components would be required to produce that amount of free energy, assuming two electrons are transferred per phosphate group esterified?

(c) Would it be sufficient to know the standard electrode reduction potentials (at pH 7.60) of the various components in the chain and to compare their differences with the value obtained in part *(b)* to determine at what step phosphorylation occurs?

8. Against how large at concentration ratio can the free energy released by the hydrolysis of P_i from one ATP molecule be used to transport an uncharged molecule such as glucose, from one side of a membrane to the other, assuming the concentrations of the principal reactants given in Problem 7?

Answers

1. $\Delta G = RT \ln \dfrac{0.1}{1}$

    $\Delta G = -1{,}364 \log 10$

    $\Delta G = -1{,}364$ cal/mole

2. ΔG^0 for conversion of A to $C = 2100 + (-2700) = -600$ cal/mole.

    ΔG^0 for conversion of E to $B = -4100 + 2100 = -2100$ cal/mole.

    Yes, both of the sequences suggested might proceed spontaneously. That is, conversion of E to A could build up sufficient concentrations of A so that its conversion to B would occur with a negative free-energy change. Continuous depletion of B by conversion to C could well also act to make negative the free-energy change of the conversion of A to B. (On the other hand, if either of the three reactions involves an obligatory intermediate, a substantial activation energy could negate the predictions, unless the needed catalysts are present.)

3. $\Delta G^0 = -2.303 \, RT \log K_{eq}$

    $\Delta G^0 = 1364(4.70) = 6411$ cal/mole

    $\Delta G' = 6411 + 1364 \log 10^{-7} = 6411 - 9548 = -3137$ cal/mole

    The reaction changes from spontaneous at pH 7 to nonspontaneous at pH 1. Equal concentrations of the dissociated and undissociated form are at equilibrium at pH 4.70. This value appears to be independent of total concentration only because we use concentrations rather than activities in its determination.

4. Since a 0.065 molal solution of picric acid in water and a 0.093 molal solution of picric acid in ether are in equilibrium with solid picric acid (presumably of the same crystalline form in the two cases), the free energy of picric acid is the same in the two solutions, and the free energy of transfer from one saturated solution to the other is zero. Calculation from $\Delta G = \Delta G^0 + RT \ln \dfrac{[\text{picric}]_{ether}}{[\text{picric}]_{water}}$ where the standard states are taken to be 1 molal picric acid in each case, gives a value of ΔG^0 of -212 cal/mole. Under the stated assumptions, ΔG will be zero whenever the molal concentrations are in the ratio 1.43:1 (the same ratio shown by their solubilities); hence the partition coefficient of picric acid is calculated as 1.43.

For benzoic acid, $\Delta G^0 = -3600$ cal/mole, and the calculated partition coefficient is 207. The error made in assuming the activities equal to the concentrations is likely to be very large, however, in this case.

5. (a) For the reaction

$Fe(CN)_6^{-4}$ + cytochrome a (oxidized) $\longrightarrow Fe(CN)_6^{-3}$ + cytochrome a (reduced)
at equilibrium,

$$E = E'_{1/2 \, cyt \ a} - E'_{1/2 \, ferrocyanide} - \frac{2.3 \, RT}{nF} \log \frac{[\text{cyt } a_{red}] \, [Fe(CN)_6^{-3}]}{[\text{cyt } a_{ox}] \, [Fe(CN)_6^{-4}]} = 0$$

From Table II (Appendix B) we note that $E'_{1/2}$ for the ferrocyanide-ferricyanide couple is 0.36 volt. We also note that $n = 1$. Therefore,

$$E'_{1/2 \, cyt \ a} = 0.36 + 0.059 \log \frac{11.5}{88.5} \times \frac{1}{2} = 0.36 + 0.059 \ \log \ 0.065 =$$
$$0.36 + 0.059(-1.187) = 0.36 - 0.07 = 0.29 \text{ volt}$$

(b) No. The large gap between two values for E' requires cytochrome b to be almost completely oxidized even if ferricyanide is almost totally reduced. Under these conditions the measurements of the concentration ratios would be quite inaccurate.

6. The maximal distribution ratio for NH_4^+ that can be generated is the same as that for H^+, namely 1000, in favor of the urine. The energy has necessarily had to be supplied to the hydrogen ion pump to create both the gradient of H^+ and that of NH_4^+.
Proof: The overall reaction can be represented by

$$(NH_3)_1 + (H^+)_1 \to (NH_4^+)_1, \ \text{plus} \ (NH_4^+)_2 \to (NH_3)_2 + (H^+)_2$$

where the subscripts 1 and 2 identify the two phases. Thus,

$$\Delta G = 2.303 \ RT \ \log \frac{[NH_4^+]_1 \cdot [H^+]_2 \cdot [NH_3]_2}{[NH_4^+]_2 \cdot [H^+]_1 \cdot [NH_3]_1}$$
(ΔG^0 being the same for the two phases)

Page 207

But $[NH_3]_1$ and $[NH_3]_2$ are equal. Hence $\Delta G = 2.303\ RT \log \dfrac{[NH_4]_1 \cdot [H^+]_2}{[NH_4]_2 \cdot [H^+]_1}$

When $\Delta G = 0$ (namely, at equilibrium), $\dfrac{[NH_4^+]_1}{[NH_4^+]_2} = \dfrac{[H^+]_1}{[H^+]_2}$

7. (a) For the reaction $ADP + P_i \rightarrow ATP + H_2O$

$$\Delta G = \Delta G^0_{pH\,7.60} + RT\ ln \frac{[ATP]\ [H_2O]}{[ADP]\ [P_i]}$$

Under the stated conditions,

$$\Delta G = 9.25 + 1.364\ \log \frac{(138 \times 10^{-6})\ (1)}{(5 \times 10^{-6})\ (670 \times 10^{-6})}$$
$$= 9.25 + 1.364\ \log\ (4.12\ \times 10^{+4})$$
$$= 9.25 + 1.364 \times 4.615 = 15.55\ \ \text{kcal/mole}$$

If you did not include the 10^{-6} factors in the concentration terms, remember ΔG^0 is calculated for 1 M concentrations of reactants, except water, which is assumed to have unit activity.

(b) One step in the electron transport chain must have a free-energy change of -15.55 kcal/mole (assuming this actually is an equilibrium and not a steady state situation). Since $\Delta G = -nFE$ and there are two equivalents of electrons transferred per mole of phosphate esterified),

$E = -\Delta G/nE$
$= 15.55\ \text{kcal mole}^{-1} / (2\ \text{eq mole}^{-1} \times 23.06\ \text{kcal volt}^{-1}\ \text{eq}^{-1})$
$= 0.337\ \text{volt}$

(c) No. You would also need at least to know the order in which electrons are transferred through the various components and the ratios of the concentrations (better, activities) of their reduced and oxidized forms so that you can determine the potential differences that exist under the conditions of the reaction. If you did then find one step with a potential difference of 0.337 volt (or more), you would have a strong indication that this was the stage at which phosphorylation occurs, although corroborating biochemical evidence would be necessary for any final conclusion.

8. Hydrolysis of the ATP at the concentrations given in the previous question would have a $\Delta G = -15.55$ kcal/mole. Therefore it could do at most 15.55 kcal/mole of work. Since the free energy required to transport a molecule across a membrane is given (Item 244) by

$$\Delta G = 2.303 \; RT \; \log \frac{[A]_2}{[A]_1}$$

then

$$\log \frac{[A]_2}{[A]_1} = \frac{15.55}{1.364} = 11.40$$

The maximum gradient that can be generated is

$$\frac{[A]_2}{[A]_1} = 2.5 \times 10^{11}$$

Provocative Questions

1. The requirement has been proposed that effluent waters discharged from the Michigan shore of Lake Michigan shall not be more than 1°F warmer than the temperature of the lake. Suppose that the principal considerations are the conservation of our energy resources and minimizing the total warming of the environment, and that we ignore the important hazard of local warming of the lake waters. Would it serve these objectives to cool effluent waters by pumping them through a cooling tower or by other mechanical refrigerating devices before discharging them into the lake?

2. The accompanying curve represents the uptake of ^{14}C-leucine by a bacterial cell suspension. Discuss factors that should be considered before deciding that the process is in fact an active transport.

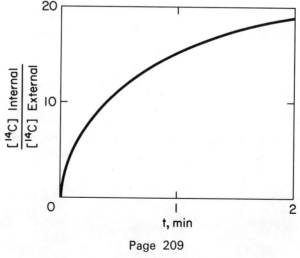

3.   In Item 116, the $\Delta G'$ for the reaction

dihydroxyacetone phosphate → glyceraldehyde-3-phosphate

is reported to be $+ 1.83$ kcal/mole.

(a) Recalling that equal amounts of the two substances are formed by the cleavage of fructose-1,6-diphosphate, would you expect *DHP* to be formed at the expense of *G3P*?

(b) Since *G3P* undergoes further transformation in the normal course of glycolysis, how can glycolysis proceed without the need for an input of energy to permit the above reaction?

4.   Twenty to thirty years ago the possibility was still being considered that the peptide link is formed through catalysis by proteolytic enzymes. Waldschmidt-Leitz and Kühn observed in 1950 that, in the presence of papain, hippuric acid reacts spontaneously with aniline to form hippurylanilide, with an apparent ΔG^0 of $- 5000$ cal / mole at 37°C. The reaction also proceeded spontaneously between hippurate and *p*-aminobenzoic acid:

$$\langle \bar{\ } \rangle CONHCH_2COO^- + H_2N\langle \bar{\ } \rangle COOH \longrightarrow$$

$$\langle \bar{\ } \rangle CONHCH_2CONH\langle \bar{\ } \rangle COOH$$

No reaction was observed, however, between hippurate and NH_4^+ or aliphatic amines. For the formation of a peptide bond between two ordinary amino acids in water solution, ΔG^0 values of $+3500$ cal/mole are typical.

Offer an explanation for the large differences in ΔG^0 in these cases. Clue: pK'_a values are as follows: for hippuric acid 3.7, for aniline 4.56, for NH_4^+ 9.4 and for most neutral amino acids about 2.3 for the carboxyl group and about 9.7 for the amino group.

5.   The chemical potential of water in tall trees is influenced not only by solute concentration and pressure, but also by height. Recall that a pressure of 1 atm is capable. of supporting a column of mercury 760 mm high, or a column of water about 10 m high (see diagram).

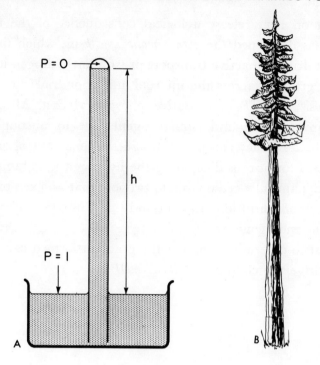

(a)   Assuming that there is no flow of water, how would μ_s^t depend on the height of the column of water?

(b)   What would be the pressure of sap in the leaf xylem at the top of a redwood tree 100 m high when it is in equilibrium with the xylem sap at the bottom of the tree ($h = 0$, $P = 1$ atm)?

(c)   What would the pressure be in the leaf parenchymal cell, where the solute concentration is about 0.5 M when there is osmotic equilibrium with the leaf xylem sap ($C = 0.041$ M)?

6.   The metabolic inhibitor 2,4-dinitrophenol acts to uncouple oxidative phosphorylation from electron transport to a greater or lesser extent, according to the dose. The result is a lowering of P to O ratios, i. e., the number of high-energy phosphate bonds formed per oxygen atom consumed, to which a normal value of 3 is ascribed. Dinitrophenol poisoning increases heat production by the experimental animal. The stimulation of heat production by the thyroid hormones may possibly occur on the same basis.

(a) Is this effect on heat release a logical consequence of the uncoupling?

Mitchell has developed the *chemiosmotic hypothesis,* which proposes that electron transport drives an active transport process for hydrogen ion, and that the resultant pH gradient across the internal mitochondrial membrane then drives the synthesis of *ATP* in oxidative phosphorylation. Mitchell further proposes that dinitrophenol and similar agents act to uncouple oxidative phosphorylation because they can pass through the inner mitochondrial membrane in protonated form, thus dissipating the hydrogen ion gradient.

(b) Is it thermodynamically reasonable to propose that an exergonic chemical reaction produce a concentration gradient and that this concentration gradient drive a subsequent endergonic reaction?

(c) Suggest a test to determine whether the gradient formed can supply sufficient energy to drive the coupling of P_i to *ADP*.

Answers

1. The cooling of effluents will of course also warm the environment. The total warming will be greater because of the energy invested in pumping the effluents through the cooling tower, or in the operation of any refrigerating device.

2. Although the time during which a distribution ratio of ten- and twenty-fold develops here is quite short, it is possible either (*a*) that the actual amounts of leucine used are so small that the leucine taken up is all bound at reactive sites— for example, of the transport carrier or of enzymes, or (*b*) that much of the leucine has already been catabolized or synthesized into protein within the first minute or two. Proof that the leucine taken up by the cell is still free leucine is at best difficult. *Uptake* cannot automatically be equipped with transport. Question: Would a finding that an inhibitor of energy metabolism interferes with uptake be decisive?

3. (a) Yes
    (b) The actual free energy change depends on the concentration of the reactants. Because *G3P* is continually being utilized, its concentration is kept low relative to that of *DHP*. Hence, the reaction above tends to proceed spontaneously in the direction shown, rather than to *DHP* formation.

4. A pH can be selected at which over 25 per cent of the hippuric acid is in the form $\langle\!\!\!\!\!\bigcirc\!\!\!\!\!\rangle CO\text{–}NHCH_2\,COOH$ and over 25 per cent of the aniline is in the form $H_2N\langle\!\!\!\!\!\bigcirc\!\!\!\!\!\rangle$. These are the reactive forms, and not $\langle\!\!\!\!\!\bigcirc\!\!\!\!\!\rangle CONHCH_2COO^-$ and $^+H_3N\langle\!\!\!\!\!\bigcirc\!\!\!\!\!\rangle$. At no pH value can one have substantial proportions of both hippurate and NH_4^+ in the reactive forms. At pH 6.0 the carboxyl group and the amino group of a typical neutral amino acid will each be present in the reactive forms to the extent of only 1 part in 5000. Hence we see that most of the free energy of hydrolysis of the peptide bond arises from the free energy of the sub-sequent spontaneous loss of H^+ from the carboxyl group and its gain by the amino group. For the purposes of peptide synthesis, the chemist seeks of course to convert the carboxyl group into a form other than $-COO^-$, e.g., by forming the acid chloride or the azo derivative, and to maintain the amino group in the uncharged form, for example by preparing the ethyl ester of the amino acid and carrying out the reaction on $H_2NCHRCOOEt$ in ether solution.

5. (a) Recall that the relationship between the height of the column and the pressure necessary to maintain it is a linear one. Therefore

$$\mu_s^t = \mu_s + \overline{V}_s(P-P_0) + kh$$

where $\mu_s = \mu_s^0 + RT\ln a_s$ and for simplicity, we set $P_0 = 0$. We still need to evaluate k. For no net flow μ_s^t is constant and for a column of pure water $\mu_s = \mu_{H_2O}^0$. Equating μ_s^t at the bottom and the top of the column we obtain

$$\mu^0{}_{H_2O} + \overline{V}_{H_2O}\,(1\text{ atm}) + k \cdot 0 =$$
$$\mu^0{}_{H_2O} + \overline{V}_{H_2O}\,(0) + k \cdot 10\text{ m}$$
$$k = 0.1\,\overline{V}_{H_2O} = 5.55\text{ liter-atm/meter}$$

(b) We take μ_s in the xylem as constant throughout the height of the tree. At equilibrium μ_s^t is the same at the top and bottom.

$$\mu^0{}_{H_2O} + \overline{V}_{H_2O}\,(P) + 0.1\,\overline{V}_{H_2O} \cdot 100 = \mu^0{}_{H_2O} + \overline{V}_{H_2O}(1) + 0.1\overline{V}_{H_2O} \cdot 0$$
$$P = 1 - 10 = -9\text{ atm}$$

(This negative value for the pressure in the leaf xylem tells us that the information supplied is insufficient for us to account for the maintenance of a column of free water molecules 100 m high. We may interpret the result to mean that the water in the leaf xylem is under tension, a tension which is attributed to cohesion of water molecules produced by hydrogen-bonding in the narrow vessels of the tree.)

(c) Equating μ_s^t in the parenchyma and xylem and using the van't Hoff equation

$$RT[\text{solute}] \simeq \Pi = -\frac{RT}{\bar{V}_s} \ln a_s$$

we obtain

$$\mu_{H_2O}^0 - RT\bar{V}_s (0.5) + \bar{V}_s P + 0.1 \bar{V}_s (100) =$$
$$\mu_{H_2O}^0 - RT\bar{V}_s (0.041) + \bar{V}_s (-9) + 0.1 \bar{V}_s (100)$$
$$P = RT (0.459) - 9$$
$$P = + 11.2 - 9 = 2.2 \quad \text{atm}$$

6. (a) Yes. Coupling implies an enhanced approach to thermodynamic reversibility, whereby the exergonic reaction is maximally restrained, causing it to drive an endergonic reaction. Removal of that restraint can be expected to permit acceleration. The thermodynamic inefficiency of partially uncoupled oxidative phosphorylation also means that more heat will be released and less work done for a given amount of fuel consumed.

(b) Yes. The sequence resembles the interposition of a concentration cell between the exergonic process and the endergonic process to which it is coupled. Thermodynamics would scarcely be worth studying if it merely gave us a more sophisticated way to state equilibrium constants. The concept of the free energy is far more valuable for the analysis it provides us of the equivalency of the potential energy stored in chemical structures and that inherent in concentration gradients.

(c) A large enough asymmetry in the distribution ratio of H^+ must be established to supply the ΔG needed for formation of a high-energy bond of ATP at the concentrations actually applicable. As Problem 8 in the preceding section brought out, a distribution ratio as high as 10^{11} might under certain conditions be required. Controversy continues whether asymmetries of H^+ distribution of sufficient magnitude are generated in the mitochondrion and the chloroplast.

APPENDIX B

TABLE 1 STANDARD ELECTRODE REDUCTION POTENTIALS AT 25°C

System (Oxidant/Reductant)	Reaction	$E_{\frac{1}{2}}^{0}$ (volts)
Ce^{4+}/Ce^{3+}	$Ce^{4+} + e^- \rightarrow Ce^{3+}$	$+ 1.61$
O_2/H_2O	$O_2 + 4H^+ + 4e^- \rightarrow 2H_2O$	$+ 1.229$
Ag^+/Ag	$Ag^+ + e^- \rightarrow Ag$	$+ 0.799$
Fe^{3+}/Fe^{2+}	$Fe^{3+} + e^- \rightarrow Fe^{2+}$	$+ 0.771$
I_2/I^-	$I_2 + 2e^- \rightarrow 2I^-$	$+ 0.536$
$Fe(CN)_6{}^{3-}/Fe(CN)_6{}^{4-}$	$Fe(CN)_6{}^{3-} + e^- \rightarrow Fe(CN)_6{}^{4-}$	$+ 0.36$
Cu^{2+}/Cu	$Cu^{2+} + 2e^- \rightarrow Cu$	$+ 0.337$
$Hg_2Cl_2/Hg, Cl^-$	$Hg_2Cl_2 + 2e^- \rightarrow 2Hg + 2Cl^-$	$+ 0.2800$
$AgCl/Ag, Cl^-$	$AgCl + e^- \rightarrow Ag + Cl^-$	$+ 0.222$
Cu^{2+}/Cu^+	$Cu^{2+} + e^- \rightarrow Cu^+$	$+ 0.153$
Sn^{4+}/Sn^{2+}	$Sn^{4+} + 2e^- \rightarrow Sn^{2+}$	$+ 0.15$
H^+/H_2	$2H^+ + 2e^- \rightarrow H_2$	0.0000(defined)
Fe^{3+}/Fe	$Fe^{3+} + 3e^- \rightarrow Fe$	$- 0.036$
Sn^{2+}/Sn	$Sn^{2+} + 2e^- \rightarrow Sn$	$- 0.136$
Fe^{2+}/Fe	$Fe^{2+} + 2e^- \rightarrow Fe$	$- 0.440$
Zn^{2+}/Zn	$Zn^{2+} + 2e^- \rightarrow Zn$	$- 0.763$
Li^+/Li	$Li^+ + e^- \rightarrow Li$	$- 3.045$

TABLE 2. STANDARD ELECTRODE REDUCTION POTENTIALS AT 25°C AND pH 7

for Systems of Biochemical Interest

System (Oxidant/Reductant)	$E'_{\frac{1}{2}}$ (volts)
O_2/H_2O	+ 0.815
Fe^{3+}/Fe^{2+}	+ 0.771
Cytochrome oxidase (Fe^{3+}/Fe^{2+})	+ 0.550
NO_3^-/NO_2^-	+ 0.42
$Fe\ (CN)_6^{3-}/Fe(CN)_6^{4-}$	+ 0.36
O_2/H_2O_2	+ 0.30
Cytochrome a (Fe^{3+}/Fe^{2+})	+ 0.29
Benzoquinone/Hydroquinone	+ 0.286
Cytochrome c (Fe^{3+}/Fe^{2+})	+ 0.260
Crotonyl-SCoA/Butyryl-SCoA	+ 0.19
Methemogloblin/Hemoglobin (Fe^{3+}/Fe^{2+})	+ 0.17
Cytochrome $b_2 (Fe^{3+}/Fe^{2+})$	+ 0.12
Coenzyme Q (quinone/hydroquinone)	+ 0.110
Dehydroascorbate/Ascorbate	+ 0.08
Metmyoglobin/Myoglobin (Fe^{3+}/Fe^{2+})	+ 0.046
Fumarate/Succinate	+ 0.03
Methylene Blue (leuco/blue)	+ 0.011
Yellow enzyme $(FMN/FMNH_2)$	− 0.122
Pyruvate + NH_4^+/Alanine	− 0.13
α-Ketoglutarate + NH_4^+/Glutamate	− 0.14
Oxaloacetate/Malate	− 0.166
Pyruvate/Lactate	− 0.190
Dihydroxyacetone phosphate/Glycerol-1-phosphate	− 0.192
Acetaldehyde/Ethanol	− 0.197
Riboflavin	− 0.21
Glutathione $(RS\text{-}SR/RSH)$	− 0.23
Acetoacetate/β-Hydroxybutyrate	− 0.27
1, 3-Diphosphoglycerate/Glyceraldehyde-3-phosphate + HPO_4^{2-}	− 0.286
Lipoic acid $(RS\text{-}SR/RSH)$	− 0.29
Acetone/2-propanol	− 0.296
$NAD^+/NADH + H^+$	− 0.320
$NADP^+/NADPH + H^+$	− 0.324
Pyruvate + CO_2/Malate	− 0.33
Uric acid/Xanthine	− 0.36
CO_2/Formate	− 0.42
H^+/H_2	− 0.42
Ferredoxin (Fe^{3+}/Fe^{2+})	− 0.43
Acetate/Acetaldehyde	− 0.60
Succinate + CO_2/α-Ketoglutarate	− 0.67
Acetate + CO_2/Pyruvate	− 0.70

APPENDIX C

Derivation of the Extended Form of the Chemical Potential

(The Total Chemical Potential)

The free energy is defined by the equation

$$G = H - TS = U + PV - TS$$

If we denote the free energy of the system at a standard pressure (P_0) and temperature (T) as G_0, and if we neglect the effect of external force fields in designating G_0, then G_0 is the free energy as considered in the bulk of the program. We can write

and
$$G_0 = U_0 + P_0V - TS$$
$$\mu_i = \mu_i^0 + RT \ln a_i$$

If we use this standard condition as a reference, then the total energy of the system will change, when an electrical potential is introduced, by an amount

$$\Delta U = \Sigma_j n_j z_j \, F\phi$$

where
  n_j = number of moles of the jth component (ion)
  z_j = electrical charge on the jth component (equivalents/mole)
  F = Faraday constant
  ϕ = electrical potential (the choice of reference level for ϕ is arbitrary; we have chosen our standard condition as the reference of zero potential, i.e., $\phi_0 = 0$)

This expression represents work done on the ions in the system when the electrical potential is introduced; its derivation can be found in any elementary physics text. If other external fields, such as gravitational or rotational fields, need to be considered explicitly, they would be added to ΔU and treated similarly.

We can now write, for the total free energy,

$$G_t = U_0 + \Delta U + PV - TS = U_0 + P_0V - TS + (P - P_0)V + \Delta U$$

where we have explicitly assumed that P (but not T) may differ from our standard conditions. Substituting for ΔU, and noting that

$$U_0 + P_0 V - TS = G_0$$

we obtain

$$G_t = G_0 + (P - P_0 V) + \Sigma_j n_j z_j F\phi$$

The total chemical potential of the ith component can then be calculated:

$$\mu_i^t = \frac{\partial G}{\partial n_i} + (P - P_0) \frac{\partial V}{\partial n_i} + \frac{\partial}{\partial n_i} [\Sigma_j n_j z_j F\phi]$$

or finally

$$\mu_i^t = \mu_i + (P - P_0) \bar{V}_i + z_i F\phi$$

where

$$\mu_i = \mu_i^0 + RT \, ln \, a_i$$

and

$$\bar{V}_i = \left(\frac{\partial \bar{V}}{\partial n_i}\right)_{P,T,n_1, n_2 \ldots, \phi}$$

is the *partial molar volume* of the ith component.

INDEX

Index

All references in this index are to page number, not to item number; (t) refers to table.

VALUES FOR SOME USEFUL CONSTANTS
AND CONVERSION FACTORS

Avogadro's number	$\mathcal{N}_0 = 6.0225 \times 10^{23}$
Boltzmann's constant	$k = 1.3805 \times 10^{-16}$ erg/K
Calorie (defined)	1 cal $= 4.1840$ absolute joules
	$= 0.041292$ liter-atm
Electronic charge	$e = 1.6021 \times 10^{-19}$ coulombs
Faraday constant	$F = \mathcal{N}_0 K = 96{,}487$ coulombs/equivalent
	$= 96{,}487$ joules/volt equivalent
	$= 23{,}061$ calories/volt equivalent
Gas constant	$R = \mathcal{N}_0 k = 8.3143$ joules/K-mole
	$= 1.9872$ cal/K-mole
	$= 0.082053$ liter-atm/K-mole
Ice point	$0°C = 273.15$ K (Kelvin or Absolute)
Molar volume of perfect gas at 0°C and 1 atm.	$V_0 = 22.413$ liters
Standard atmosphere (pressure)	1 atm $= 1{,}013{,}250$ dynes /cm^2
	$= 1.013250$ bars
	$= 760$ mm of Hg at 0°C
	$= 10.33$ m of H_2O at 4°C
Logarithmic conversions	$ln\ x = 2.3026 \log x$
	$\log x = 0.434229\ ln\ x$
Frequently used factors	$R\ ln\ x = 19.145 \log x$ joules /K-mole
	$= 4.5757 \log x$ cal/K-mole
	$R/F\ ln\ x = 0.00019841 \log x$ volt/K
At 0°C	$RT = 22.413$ liter-atm/mole
	$= 542.80$ cal/mole
	$= 2271.1$ joules/mole
At 25°C = 298.15 K	$RT = 24.464$ liter-atm/mole
	$= 592.48$ cal/mole
	$= 2478.9$ joules/mole
	$RT\ ln\ x = 5708 \log x$ joules/mole
	$= 1364 \log x$ cal/mole
	$\dfrac{RT}{F}\ ln\ x = 0.059157 \log x$ volt